CW00750590

ROUND-UP 1
CONTENTS

Introduction

Round-up Grammar Practice 1 combines games and fun with serious, systematic grammar practice. It is ideal for students at the early stages of English language learning.

Students see grammar points clearly presented in colourful boxes and tables. They practise grammar through lively, highly illustrated games and activities.

Round-up is especially designed for different students studying English in different ways.

It can be used:
● in class with a coursebook. Students do both oral work – in pairs and in groups – and written work in Round-up.
● after class. The 'write-in' activities are ideal for homework. Students can practise what they have learned in the classroom.
● in the holidays for revision. Round-up has clear instructions and simple grammar boxes, so students can study at home without a teacher.

The Round-up Teacher's Guide includes a full answer key and four tests plus answer keys.

Pearson Education Limited
Edinburgh Gate, Harlow
Essex CM20 2JE England
and Associated Companies throughout the world.

www.longman.com

First published in 1992 by B & E. Vlachou - "Express Publishers".
First published by Longman Group Limited 1995.
This edition published by Pearson Education Limited 2003.

Fifth impression 2006

Printed in Spain
by Mateu Cromo

Illustrated by Chris Zmertis and Terry Wilson

ISBN-13: 978-0-582-82344-0
ISBN-10: 0-582-82344-7

1. A - An

a + consonant	an + vowel (a, e, i, o, u)

a **c**lown   a **b**ook   an **a**pple   an **u**mbrella

 Add "a" or "an".

1. ...*an*.. onion   2. .... cat   3. .... baby   4. .... armchair

5. .... iron   6. .... lion   7. .... dog   8. .... fish

9. .... eye   10. .... car   11. .... tree   12. .... duck

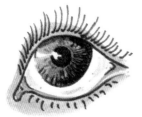   

13. .... lemon   14. .... ear   15. .... octopus   16. .... eagle

Choose one word from the box below and write it under each picture. Put "a" or "an" before each word.

orange	apple	zebra	man	boy	egg	book	owl
snake	horse	umbrella	cat	banana	aeroplane	elephant	

1. ......*a snake*......　　2. ....　　3. ....

4. ....　　5. ....　　6. ....

7. ....　　8. ....　　9. ....

10. ....　　11. ....　　12. ....

13. ....　　14. ....　　15. ....

2. Plural Forms

 A **Most nouns form their plural by adding -s**

Singular

one penguin

Plural

two penguins

3 **Complete the plural as in the example:**

1. One balloon four *balloons*   2. One tree two ....   3. One cat two ....

4. One frog three ....   5. One bird two ....   6. One star three ....

7. One book two ....   8. One cow two ....   9. One chair two ....

10. One rabbit three ....   11. One doll two ....   12. One ball four ....

Nouns ending in:

 B **consonant + y ➡ ies but vowel (a,e,i,o,u) + y ➡ s**

Singular	Plural
baby	babies

BUT

Singular	Plural
boy	boys

2. Plural Forms

 s,ss,sh,ch,x,o ➡ **es**

Singular	Plural	Singular	Plural
bus	buses	church	churches
glass	glasses	box	boxes
bush	bushes	tomato	tomatoes

 f / fe ➡ **ves**

Singular	Plural
leaf	leaves
housewife	housewives

④ Complete the plural as in the example:

1. One boy ● two ..*boys*..   2. One baby ● two ....   3. One brush ● two ....

4. One tomato ● two ....   5. One radio ● two ....   6. One box ● two ....

7. One leaf ● two ....   8. One knife ● four ....   9. One torch ● two ....

Irregular Plurals

 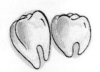  

tooth ● **teeth**   *man* ● **men**   *policeman* ● **policemen**

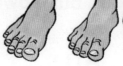  

mouse ● **mice**   *foot* ● **feet**   *woman* ● **women**

child • **children**   *goose* • **geese**   *ox* • **oxen**

  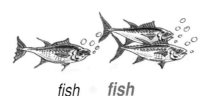 

sheep • **sheep**   *fish* • **fish**   *deer* • **deer**

⑤ Change to the plural as in the example:

1. One woman two ...*women*   2. One goose three ....   3. One child three ....

4. One mouse three ....   5. One man two ....   6. One tooth two ....

⑥ Change to the plural as in the example:

1. One hat two ...*hats*......   2. One glass three ....   3. One bus two ....

4. One boy three ....   5. One hand two ....   6. One dress two ....

7. One mouse two ....   8. One watch three ....   9. One sheep two ....

3. Personal Pronouns

Singular	Plural
I	we
you	you
he	they
she	
it	

7 Write "he", "she", "it" or "they" as in the example:

1. ..... *it* .....   2. ....   3. ....   4. ....

5. ....   6. ....   7. ....   8. ....

9. . . . .
10. . . . .
11. . . . .
12. . . . .

13. . . . .
14. . . . .
15. . . . .
16. . . . .

17. . . . .
18. . . . .
19. . . . .
20. . . . .

21. . . . .
22. . . . .
23. . . . .

8 **Fill in "he", "she", "it", "we", "you" or "they" as in the example:**

1. Helen . . *she* . .	9. Tom and I	17. school . . . . . .
2. Sam	10. car	18. apples . . . . . .
3. Father	11. dogs	19. book . . . . . .
4. Mother	12. you and Jane	20. Nick and I . . . . . .
5. Father and Mother	13. ball	21. children . . . . . .
6. Ann and Tom	14. plane	22. feet . . . . . .
7. clowns	15. sister	23. guitar . . . . . .
8. pen	16. brother	24. Mary . . . . . .

4. The verb "to be"

Affirmative		Negative		Interrogative
Long form	**Short form**	**Long form**	**Short form**	
I am	I'm	I am not	I'm not	Am I?
You are	You're	You are not	You aren't	Are you?
He is	He's	He is not	He isn't	Is he?
She is	She's	She is not	She isn't	Is she?
It is	It's	It is not	It isn't	Is it?
We are	We're	We are not	We aren't	Are we?
You are	You're	You are not	You aren't	Are you?
They are	They're	They are not	They aren't	Are they?

(9) Fill in "am", "is" or "are".

1. It ..*is*.. a shark.   2. They .... dolphins. 3. It .... a bicycle.   3. They ... oranges.

5. We ..... friends.　6. It ..... a bus.　7. I ..... a teacher.　8. You ..... a doctor.

 First read about Jane, then write about you.

..I am Jane. I am ten. I am a student. ....
..I am English and I am from London. ....

Jane
10
student
England
London

I ....

....

....

Write about your friend.

....

....

....

Short answers	Am I / Are you tall?	Yes, I am.	No, I'm not.
	Is he / she / it in the garden?	Yes, he / she / it is.	No, he / she / it isn't.
	Are **we / you** / **they** students?	Yes, **we / you** / **they** are.	No, **we / you** / **they** aren't.

 Answer the questions:

1.  Is it a mouse?
　..Yes, it is. ....
　. . . . .

2. Are they horses?
　.No, they aren't. ..
　.They are dogs.....

3.  Are you a teacher?
　. . . . .
　. . . . .

4. Is it a bird?
　. . . . .
　. . . . .

4. The verb "to be"

5. Is Pam a student?

....

....

6. Is Paul at home?

....

....

7. Are they records?

....

....

8. Are you doctors?

....

....

12 **Write "is" or "are" as in the example:**

Ann	Manos	Mario	Susan	Costas	Kim
10	28	12	25	13	25
student	teacher	student	teacher	student	doctor
English	Greek	Italian	American	Greek	Japanese
London	Athens	Rome	New York	Thessaloniki	Tokyo

Ann .. *is* .. ten years old.

1. Ann, Mario and Costas .... students.   2. Manos .... a teacher.   3. Susan and Manos .... teachers.   4. Manos and Costas .... Greek.   5. Kim .... Japanese. She .... from Tokyo.   6. Mario .... Italian. He .... from Rome.   7. Manos .... from Athens and Costas .... from Thessaloniki.   8. Susan .... American. She .... from New York.   9. Susan and Kim .... twenty-five years old.   10. Mario .... twelve and Costas .... thirteen.

13 **Look at Exercise 12. Then ask and answer as in the examples:**

1. Ann / a doctor. ... *Is Ann a doctor? No, she isn't a doctor. She is a student.*
2. Mario and Costas / students. .. *Are Mario and Costas students? Yes, they are.*
3. Susan / American. ....
4. Kim / from Athens. ....
5. Susan and Manos / teachers. ....

6. Ann and Mario / Greek. ....

7. Manos / New York. ....

8. Kim / a student. ....

9. Manos / a doctor. ....

10. Costas / thirteen years old. ....

(14) Look at Exercise 12 and fill in "is", "isn't", "are" or "aren't".

1. Ann ..*isn't*.. a doctor. She ..*is*... a student.   2. Manos .... a student. He
.... a teacher.   3. Susan and Kim .... students. They .... teachers.
4. Ann .... from Athens. She .... from London.   5. Kim .... ten years old.
She .... twenty-five.   6. Ann, Mario and Costas .... doctors. They ....
students.   7. Manos and Costas .... English. They .... Greek.   8. Susan and
Kim .... thirteen years old. They .... twenty-five.

(15) Change to the plural as in the example:

It is a book.   ..*They are books.*..

1. He is a man.	4. It is a mouse.	7. He is a boy.	10. You are a doctor.
2. She is a girl.	5. You are a student.	8. It is a bird.	11. She is a nurse.
3. I am a teacher.	6. I am Spanish.	9. She is a woman.	12. It's a piano.

(16) Fill in as in the example:

Long form	**Short form**
I ..*am not*..... a student.	I ..*'m not*..... a student.
1. They .... chairs.	They .... chairs.
2. We .... English.	We .... English.
3. She .... ten years old.	She .... ten years old.
4. It .... an orange.	It .... an orange.
5. You .... from London.	You .... from London.

Game 1

The teacher chooses a leader and divides the class into two groups, group A and group B. The teacher writes a singular or plural noun on a piece of paper (e.g. chairs) which is given to the leader. Then the teacher invites the students to guess what he / she has writen by asking the leader questions in turn. The students can ask the leader ten questions in order to find the word.

Group A S1:	Is it singular or plural?	Leader:	No, they aren't.
Leader:	Plural.	Group B S2:	Are they chairs?
Group B S1:	Are they books?	Leader:	Yes, they are.
Leader:	No, they aren't.		
Group A S2:	Are they apples?	Group B is the winner.

Revision I

17 **Fill in as in the example:**

1. .....*a book*..... 2. .... 3. .... 4. ....

5. .... 6. .... 7. .... 8. ....

9. .... 10. .... 11. .... 12. ....

18 **Change to the plural as in the example:**

1. cat   *cats* ....
2. frog   ....
3. book   ....
4. glass   ....
5. baby   ....
6. church   ....
7. bird   ....

8. star   ....
9. piano   ....
10. photo   ....
11. bush   ....
12. tomato ....
13. chair   ....
14. tree   ....

15. doll   ....
16. boy   ....
17. radio   ....
18. ball   ....
19. cow   ....
20. dress   ....
21. potato ....

19 **Fill in "I", "you", "he", "she", "it", "we", or "they".**

1. Greg   ..*he*....
2. you and I ....
3. cat   ....
4. man   ....
5. Steve and I ....
6. policeman ....

7. car   ....
8. Eva and I ....
9. John   ....
10. John and Charlie ....
11. Father and I ....
12. skirt   ....

13. dog   ....
14. hat   ....
15. David   ....
16. Joanna   ....
17. books   ....
18. tooth   ....

20 **Write "is" or "are" as in the example:**

Peter	Helen	Greg	Joanna
18	12	30	30
student	student	doctor	teacher
American	Spanish	Greek	English
Los Angeles	Madrid	Athens	London

Peter ..*is*.. eighteen years old.

1. Helen .... from Madrid.
2. Joanna .... a teacher.
3. Peter and Helen .... students.
4. Helen .... Spanish.
5. Greg .... from Athens.

6. Joanna .... English.
7. Peter .... from Los Angeles.
8. Greg .... thirty years old.
9. Helen .... a student.
10. Joanna and Greg .... thirty years old.

21 **Change to the plural as in the example:**

It is a pen.   ..... *They are pens.* ...

1. It is a cow.   ....
2. It is an apple.   ....
3. She is a girl.   ....
4. He is a child.   ....
5. It is a doll.   ....

6. It is a glass.   ....
7. It is a dress.   ....
8. He is a teacher.   ....
9. It is a bicycle.   ....
10. He is a man.   ....

22 **Fill in "am", "is" or "are".**

1. Tony ....*is*.... a student.
2. I .... a girl.
3. You .... from England.
4. He .... my friend.
5. Sally .... my sister.

6. We .... Spanish.
7. They .... students.
8. The dog .... black.
9. I .... English.
10. John and Joanna .... teachers.

23 **Write as in the example:**

Mr Smith is a teacher.   .. *He is a teacher* ... .

1. **Jane** is my friend.

....

2. **Tom and I** are doctors.

....

3. **Ian and Andrew** are English.

....

4. **The cat** is three years old.

....

5. **Michael** is American.

....

6. **Carolin and I** are students.

....

7. **Mrs Brown** is twenty-five.

....

8. **Robert and Tom** are friends.

....

9. **Jenny** is a nurse.

....

10. **Bill** is a boy.

....

24 **Ask and answer as in the example:**

1. (at work / at home)
   Is he at work?..................
   No he isn't. He is at home. .....

2. (at the cinema / at the theatre)

....
....

3. (in the park / at the zoo)

....
....

4. (at school / in the park)

....
....

5. (at the disco / at the café)

....
....

(25) Choose the correct pronoun.

1. ....*We*.... are doctors.
  A) It   B) We   C) She

2. .... is ten years old.
  A) He   B) We   C) They

3. .... is a hat.
  A) You   B) It   C) I

4. .... are books.
  A) They   B) We   C) She

5. Where is Jane? .... is at school.
  A) It   B) She   C) He

6. What is this? .... is a bicycle.
  A) She   B) It   C) They

7. This is Angela. .... is my friend.
  A) He   B) It   C) She

8. Where is the pen? .... is in my bag.
  A) We   B) He   C) It

9. .... are sisters.
  A) We   B) It   C) He

10. .... is a rabbit.
  A) We   B) I   C) It

11. .... is a good boy.
  A) She   B) They   C) He

12. Hello, ... am Sam.
  A) It   B) I   C) He

13. .... is a black cat.
  A) We   B) He   C) It

14. Where's the bird? .... is in the cage.
  A) She   B) They   C) It

26 **Look at the pictures and write as in the example:**

1. ..*They are children*.. 2. .... 3. ....

4. .... 5. .... 6. ....

7. .... 8. .... 9. ....

27 **Look at the pictures first, then ask and answer as in the examples:**

1. ...*Is it a*.... helicopter? 2. .*Are they*... oranges? 3. .... birds?
.*Yes, it's a helicopter*.. ..*No they aren't*. ... .
...*They are apples*... ....

4. .... child? 5. .... bicycles? 6. .... horses?
....
....

5. This – These / That – Those

This – These	That – Those
This (near) — **This** is a rabbit.	**That** (far) — **That** is a cat.
These (near) — **These** are rabbits.	**Those** (far) — **Those** are cats.

28 Fill in "this", "these", "that", or "those" as in the example:

1. ...*This*... is a cat.

2. .... is a dog.

3. .... are tables.

4. .... are bananas.

5. .... is a bed.

6. .... are chairs.

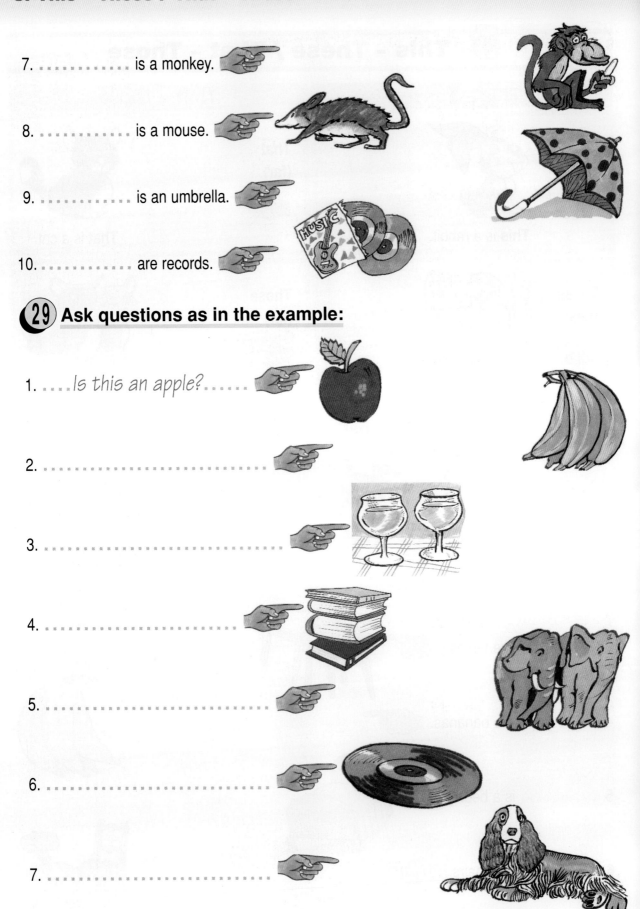

7. .... is a monkey.

8. .... is a mouse.

9. .... is an umbrella.

10. .... are records.

29 **Ask questions as in the example:**

1. .....Is this an apple?.......

2. ....

3. ....

4. ....

5. ....

6. ....

7. ....

(30) Ask and answer as in the examples:

1. 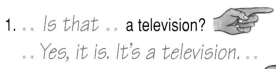 *.. Is that ..* a television?
   .. Yes, it is. It's a television. ..

2. *.. Is this ...* a bicycle?
   .. No, it isn't. It's a monkey...

3. .... apples?
   ....

4. .... bicycles?
   ....

5. .... watches?
   ....

6. .... snakes?
   ....

7. .... a lemon?
   ....

8. .... lemons?
   ....

9. .... tomatoes?
   ....

10. .... records?
    ....

6. There is – There are

	Affirmative		Negative		Interrogative
	Long form	**Short form**	**Long form**	**Short form**	
singular	there is	there's	there is not	there isn't	Is there?
plural	there are		there are not	there aren't	Are there?

31 Fill in "there is" or "there are".

..There is .... a teacher in the classroom.

1. . . . . a blackboard in the classroom.
2. . . . . five books in the classroom.
3. . . . . three desks in the classroom.
4. . . . . five boys in the classroom.
5. . . . . a chair in the classroom.
6. . . . . two windows in the classroom.

32 Write about your classroom.

. . . .

. . . .

(33) Look at the picture, ask and answer as in the examples:

three sheep? ...*Are there three sheep?*
No, there aren't. There are two sheep.

1. three ducks? ....

....

2. two dogs? ....

....

3. one cat? ....

....

4. two cows? ....

....

5. one donkey? ....

....

one man? ... *Is there one man?*.......
.... *Yes, there is.*............

6. one bird? ....

....

7. one rabbit? ....

....

8. three trees? ....

....

9. two children? ....

....

10. three hens? ....

....

7. "Have got"

Jean **has got** a ball.
Jim **has got** a train.

Have they got a bird?

No, **they haven't got** a bird. **They have got** a rabbit.

Affirmative		Negative		Interrogative
Long form	**Short form**	**Long form**	**Short form**	
I have got	I've got	I have not got	I haven't got	Have I got?
You have got	You've got	You have not got	You haven't got	Have you got?
He has got	He's got	He has not got	He hasn't got	Has he got?
She has got	She's got	She has not got	She hasn't got	Has she got?
It has got	It's got	It has not got	It hasn't got	Has it got?
We have got	We've got	We have not got	We haven't got	Have we got?
You have got	You've got	You have not got	You haven't got	Have you got?
They have got	They've got	They have not got	They haven't got	Have they got?

(34) **Fill in the blanks with** *"have got"* **or** *"has got"* **as in the example:**

1. You ...*have got*... two eyes.

2. John .... a book.

3. They .... a brother.

4. He .... a sister.

5. I .... friends.

6. We .... a house.

7. The teacher .... a car.

8. They .... watches.

9. Mr Black .... a helicopter.

10. You .... a bicycle.

(35) **Look at the picture, first say and then write what they** *have got*.

Jane ... *has got a cat.* ....

1. Jim ....

2. Tom and Julie ....

3. Mr and Mrs Green ....

4. Jennifer and Helen......................

5. George..

6. Ann...

7. Andrew..

8. Simon..

(36) **Fill in the blanks as in the example:**

Long form	Short form
1. I ..*have got*.... a telephone.	I *'ve got*........ a telephone.
2. He .... a balloon.	He .... a balloon.
3. We .... a bicycle.	We .... a bicycle.
4. You .... friends.	You .... friends.
5. Mary .... an umbrella.	Mary .... an umbrella.
6. I ..*have not got*.. a ball.	I ..*haven't got*... a ball.
7. She .... a radio.	She .... a radio.
8. We .... a helicopter.	We .... a helicopter.
9. They .... a sister.	They .... a sister.
10. They .... a sister.	They .... a sister.
11. Dave .... a brother.	John .... a brother.
12. Lydia and Mark .... a computer.	Lydia and Mark .... a computer.

25

7. *"Have got"*

Short answers	Yes, I / we have.	Yes, he / she / it has.
	No, I / we haven't.	No, he / she / it hasn't.

(37) **Ask questions and answer with short answers as in the examples:**

1. Ann / a pencil?

..Has Ann got a...
..pencil? ....
..Yes, she has. ....
....

2. the boys / a cat?

.Have the boys ....
.got a cat? ....
.No, they haven't...
.They've got a bird.

3. you / flowers?

....
....
....
....

4. she / a car?

....
....
....
....

5. Tom / a guitar?

....
....
....
....

6. you / a kite?

....
....
....
....

7. he / a ball?

....
....
....
....

8. they / hats?

....
....
....
....

9. the girl / a camera?

....
....
....
....

10. the boy / a picture?

....
....
....
....

26

38 First say and then write questions and answers as in the example:

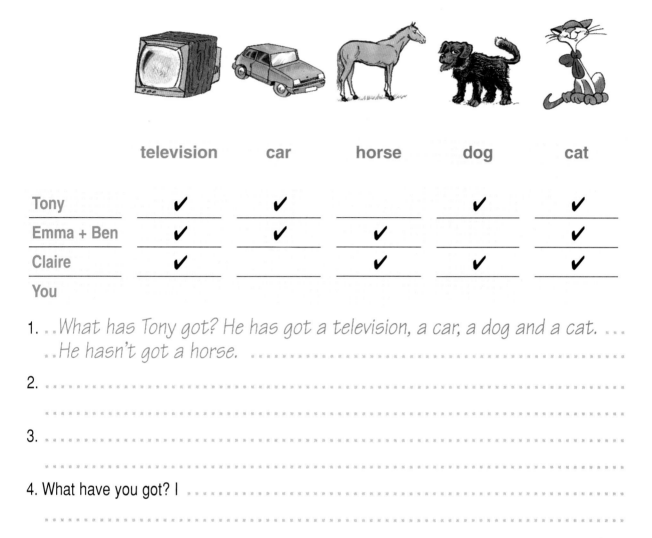

	television	car	horse	dog	cat
Tony	✔	✔		✔	✔
Emma + Ben	✔	✔	✔		✔
Claire	✔		✔	✔	✔
You					

1. ..What has Tony got? He has got a television, a car, a dog and a cat. ...
   ..He hasn't got a horse.

2.

3.

4. What have you got? I

Game 2

The teacher divides the class into two groups. The first student says an object. Groups in turn add one object each time. If they fail to remember the objects mentioned besides adding a new object, they lose 1 point. The group with the most points is the winner.

Group A S1:   I've got an apple.
Group B S1:   I've got an apple and an orange.
Group A S2:   I've got an apple, an orange and an egg.
Group B S2:   I've got an apple, an orange, an egg and a book.
Group A S3:   I've got an apple, an orange, a book and a pen.
Teacher: You've missed "egg". Group A loses 1 point.

8. Possessives

That isn't your hat. That is Dad's hat. It's his hat.

That isn't your dress. That is Mum's dress. It's her dress.

Susan give me my dress, please!

John, give me my hat, please!

Personal pronouns		Possessive adjectives		Possessive pronouns	
I	we	my	our	mine	ours
you	you	your	your	yours	yours
he	they	his	their	his	theirs
she		her		hers	
it		its		—	

Possessive case

We use **'s** with one person or animal:	We use **s'** with more than one person or animal:
Mary**'s** shoes the cat**'s** tail	the boys**'** shoes **BUT** the men**'s** hats

(39) **Look at the pictures and write sentences as in the example:**

1. Peter

cat

.This is Peter's cat.
.It's his cat......
.This cat is his. ..

2. the girls   dolls   . . . .

3. Simon   bus   . . . .

4. the boys   books   . . . .

5. Mr Brown   radio   . . . .

6. Rose   dog   . . . .

7. the horse   tail   . . . .

8. the dog   food   . . . .

9. the children   shoes   . . . .

8. Possessives

10. Mother  hat  . . . .

. . . .

. . . .

40 **Look at the pictures and write as in the example:**

1. I've got an . . . .
.umbrella. . . . .
.It's my umbrella. . .

2. She . . . .
. . . .
. . . .

3. They . . . .
. . . .
. . . .

4. He . . . .
. . . .
. . . .

5. They . . . .
. . . .
. . . .

6. They . . . .
. . . .
. . . .

7. You . . . .
. . . .
. . . .

8. We . . . .
. . . .
. . . .

9. He . . . .
. . . .
. . . .

10. I . . . .
. . . .
. . . .

41 **Underline the correct word as in the example:**

1. John is (my, mine) friend.
2. This car is (their, theirs).
3. It is Ann's dress. It's (her, hers) dress.

4. These shirts are (your, yours).
5. This is (our, ours) house. It's (our, ours).
6. This is John's bed. It's (his, her) bed.

7. The white T-shirt is (my, mine).

8. Jim is (their, theirs) son.

9. (My, Mine) skirt is red.

10. This is Jane's bag. It's (her, hers) bag.

42 **Fill in as in the example:**

(He) .. *His* ..... father is a doctor.

1. (I) .... sister is ten years old.

2. (They) .... car is red.

3. (You) .... bicycles are old.

4. (She) .... house is big.

5. (He) .... eyes are blue.

6. (We) .... dog is white.

7. (He) .... mother is a lawyer.

8. (They) .... brother is tall.

9. (I) .... house is small.

10. (We) .... cat is black.

43 **Underline the correct word as in the example:**

1. It is (her, hers) cat.

2. That is (his, her) bag. It is Jane's bag.

3. This car is (my, mine).

4. It is Jane's coat. It is (her, hers).

5. The black skirt is (my, mine).

6. Jim is (her, hers) son.

7. The red shirt is (your, yours).

8. This book is (my, mine).

9. This is (my, mine) bed.

10. Jane is (hers, her) daughter.

11. The white shirt is (his, her).

12. Toby is Jane's dog. It is (her, hers) dog.

13. (My, mine) dog is black.

14. This dog is (their, theirs).

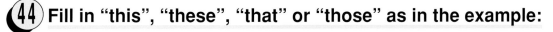

Revision II

44 **Fill in "this", "these", "that" or "those" as in the example:**

..*This* ..... is a table.

1. .... are rabbits.

2. .... is a tree.

3. .... are eyes.

4. .... is a bicycle.

5. .... are bananas.

6. .... is a record.

7. .... are books.

8. .... is an umbrella.

9. .... are dresses.

10. .... is a bed.

45 **Change to the plural as in the example:**

1. There is a pen on the desk.   *..There are pens on the desks. ....*
2. That is a bird.   ....
3. She is a girl.   ....
4. He is a student.   ....
5. It is a horse.   ....
6. This is a box.   ....

46 **Fill in "a" or "an".**

1. ..*a*..dress	3. .... orange	5. .... onion	7. .... baby
2. .... dolphin	4. .... animal	6. .... egg	8. .... umbrella

47 **Look at the picture and fill in "there is" or "there are".**

.... *There are* ......two people in the room.   1. .... a sofa in the room.   2. ....a table in the room.   3. .... two dogs in the room.   4. ....a vase on the table. 5. .... four chairs in the room.   6. .... four glasses on the table.   7. .... a baby in the room. 8. .... a radio in the room.   9. .... flowers in the vase.   10. .... a cat on the chair.

48 **Fill in "have got" or "has got" as in the example:**

I . *have got*...... a car.

1. Ben .... a bicycle.
2. We .... a cat.
3. They .... a T.V.
4. Jane .... an apple.
5. Tony .... a horse.

6. Mary and Linda .... a radio.
7. He .... a car.
8. Bill .... a watch.
9. She .... a pencil.
10. We .... a ball.

49 **Underline the correct word as in the example:**

1. She is (<u>my</u>, mine) sister.
2. The ball is (their, theirs).
3. This is (my, mine) pen. It's (my, mine).
4. This is (our, ours) T.V. It's (our, ours).
5. Mr Smith is (their, theirs) father.

6. This is Susan's cat. It's (her, hers).
7. (My, Mine) eyes are blue.
8. This umbrella is (you, yours).
9. This is Sam's ball. It's (his, hers).
10. This is (our, ours) house. It's (our, ours).

50 **Look at the table below and answer the questions.**

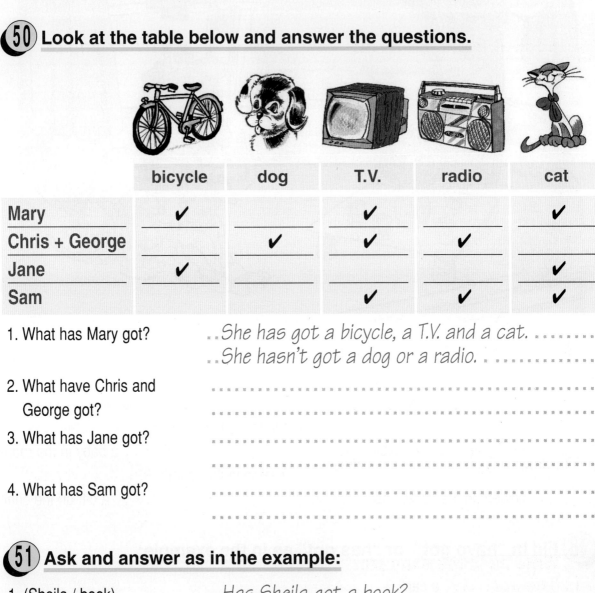

	bicycle	dog	T.V.	radio	cat
Mary	✔		✔		✔
Chris + George		✔	✔	✔	
Jane	✔				✔
Sam			✔	✔	✔

1. What has Mary got?   ..*She has got a bicycle, a T.V. and a cat.* ....
   ..*She hasn't got a dog or a radio.* ....

2. What have Chris and George got?

3. What has Jane got?

4. What has Sam got?

51 **Ask and answer as in the example:**

1. (Sheila / book)   ..*Has Sheila got a book?* ....
   ..*Yes, that's her book. It's hers.* ....

2. (John / dog)

3. (They / T.V.)

4. (Ann / doll) ....
....

5. (They / car) ....
....

6. (Tim / pen) ....
....

(52) Look at the pictures and write sentences as in the example:

1. the girls ... house

This is the girls' house.
..It's their house.......

2. John ... car
....
....

3. Mary ... doll
....
....

4. Mrs Brown ... dress
....
....

(53) Write as in the example:

1. **Paul** is twelve years old.   *...He is twelve years old. ....*

2. **The cat** is in the house.   ....

3. **The children** are in the park.   ....

4. **Susan and I** are friends.   ....

5. **Helen** is my friend.   ....

6. **The horses** are on the farm.   ....

54 **Look at the example and write.**

name: _George_   .He is George. ....
age: _12_   .He is 12. ....
eyes: _brown_   .His eyes are brown. ....
hair: _black_   .His hair is black. ....

1. name: _Helen_   ....
   age: _15_   ....
   eyes: _blue_   ....
   hair: _red_   ....

2. names: _Jim, Mary_ ....
   age: _20_   ....
   eyes: _blue_   ....
   hair: _brown_   ....

3. name:..................... ....
                              ....
   age: ....
   eyes: ....

PUT YOUR PHOTO HERE

4. name:..................... ....
                              ....
   age: ....
   eyes: ....

PUT YOUR FRIEND'S PHOTO HERE

55 **Fill in "he", "she", "it", "we" or "they".**

1. Where is the cat? .It.. is in the tree.
2. Who is Tony? ...... is my brother.
3. Is Andrew here? No, ... isn't.
4. Where is Sally? ...... is at school.
5. Is that your T.V.? Yes, ... is.
6. Is this Tony's record? No, ... isn't.
7. Is this an apple? No, ... is an orange.

8. Who is Ben? ...... is my brother.
9. Are the children at home? Yes, ... are.
10. Are you and Sally sisters? Yes, ... are.
11. Is the flower blue? Yes, ... is.
12. Where is the horse? ...... is on the farm.
13. Is Mary twelve ? No, ... is eleven.
14. Are these your cats? No, ... are Jenny's

56 **Look at the table and complete the sentences as in the example:**

	brothers' names	age	sisters' names	age
Liz	Joe	13	Jean, Kate	16, 18
1. John			Jennifer	10
2. Sally + Helen	Sam, Ben	14, 15		
3. You				

Liz   *Liz has got one brother. His name is Joe. He is 13.*
Liz has got two sisters. Their names are Jean and Kate.
Jean is 16 and Kate is 18.

1. John ....

....

....

2. Sally and Helen ....

....

....

3. Write about you:

I ....

....

....

57 **Choose the correct item.**

1. ...... *There is* ... a book on the table.
   A) There are   B) There is   C) It is

2. This is .... car.
   A) John   B) Johns'   C) John's

3. She .... a red dress.
   A) has got   B) have got   C) is

4. I .... a doctor.
   A) is   B) have got   C) am

5. This is .... elephant.
   A) a   B) that   C) an

6. There are two .... on the table.
   A) tomatoes   B) tomatos   C) tomato

7. Kate .... from Italy.
   A) am not   B) is   C) are

8. Jenny is .... sister.
   A) my   B) mine   C) you

9. These shoes are ....
   A) he   B) his   C) her

10. Are .... friends?
    A) they   B) she   C) he

"Can"

Affirmative	Negative		Interrogative
	Long form	**Short form**	
I can	I cannot	I can't	Can I?
You can	You cannot	You can't	Can you?
He can	He cannot	He can't	Can he?
She can	She cannot	She can't	Can she?
It can	It cannot	It can't	Can it?
We can	We cannot	We can't	Can we?
You can	You cannot	You can't	Can you?
They can	They cannot	They can't	Can they?

Short answers	Can you drive?	Yes, I can.
		No, I can't.

58 **Ask and answer questions as in the example:**

1. (he / run)

..Can he run?....
..Yes, he can.....

2. (they / walk)

.Can they walk?..
.No, they can't.....

3. (he / swim)

. . . .

. . . .

4. (you / ride a horse)

. . . .

. . . .

5. (he / climb)

....

....

6. (Ann / sing)

....

....

7. (you / jump)

....

....

8. (he / drive)

....

....

59 **Look at the picture and answer the questions as in the example:**

1. Can you see a bus? *No, I can't see a bus.*

2. Can you see a dog? ....

3. Can you see a bird? ....

4. Can you see a rabbit? ....

5. Can you see a woman? ....

6. Can you see a cat? ....

7. Can you see a girl? ....

8. Can you see two trees? ....

9. Can you see a baby? ....

10. Can you see a boy? ....

9. "Can"

60 **Write sentences as in the example:**

1. Dogs can drive.   ..*Wrong! Dogs can't drive.* ....
2. Helicopters can fly.   ..*Right! Helicopters can fly.* ....
3. Camels can read.   ....
4. Babies can write.   ....
5. Birds can fly.   ....
6. Elephants can ride bicycles. ....
7. Dolphins can swim.   ....

61 **Look at the table below, then ask and answer questions.**

	Jean	Bob	John + Kate	Patchy	You
read	✔	✔	✔		
swim	✔	✔		✔	
drive		✔	✔		
dance	✔		✔		

..*Can Jean read? Yes, she can.* ..

1. ....   8. ....
2. ....   9. ....
3. ....   10. ....
4. ....   11. ....
5. ....   12. ....
6. ....   13. ....
7. ....   14. ....

Now complete the above table about you and answer the questions.

1. Can you read? ....   3. Can you drive? ....
2. Can you swim? ....   4. Can you dance? ....

10. Imperative

| Close the door, please! | Please don't talk! | Let's play tennis! |

62 Match the following with the pictures.

Close the window, please!   Let's run into the house!   Come here, please!
Let's go to the supermarket!   Clean your room, please!   Please don't eat so much!
Please don't sit on that chair!   Eat your breakfast, please!   Let's work in the garden!

Let's run into the house!

1.
2.
3.

4.
5.
6. SUPERMARKET

7.
8.
9.

(63) Match the following with the pictures.

Let's sit on the sofa!
Let's listen to these records!
Give me a glass of water, please!

Buy me a hamburger, please!
Let's dance!
Clean the floor, please!

Do your homework, please!
Wash the dishes, please!
Go to bed, please!

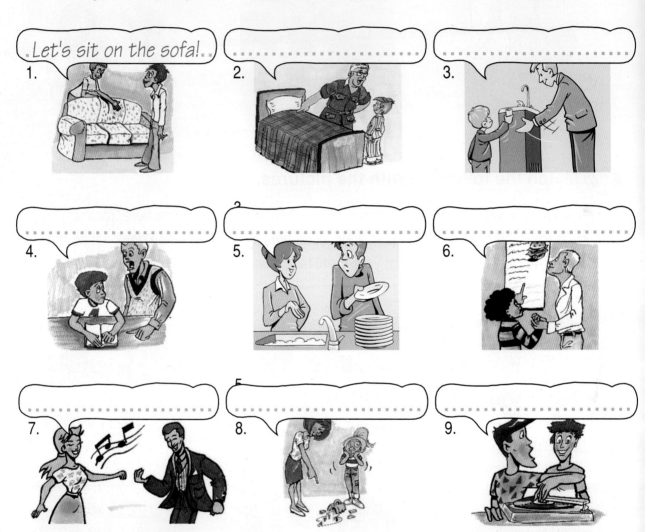

Game 3

Your teacher divides the class into two groups. Then he asks a student to come to the front of the class. He whispers in his / her ear the verb "**drive**". The students, by asking questions, must guess what he / she can do. The group which finds out what the verb is wins 1 point.

Group A S1:	Can you read?	Group A S2:	Can you dance?
Leader:	No, I can't.	Leader:	No, I can't.
Group B S1:	Can you swim?	Group B S2:	Can you drive?
Leader:	No, I can't.	Leader:	Yes, I can.

Group B wins. Your teacher may choose another leader and you can play the game again.

11. Present Continuous

I am doing my homework, mum is working and she is playing tennis. What are you doing John?

I am sitting and resting.

Father is digging in the garden and I am washing the car. What are you doing Helen?

I am sitting and resting. I am tired .

Affirmative		Negative		Interrogative
Long form	**Short form**	**Long form**	**Short form**	
I am working	I'm working	I am not working	I'm not working	Am I working?
You are working	You're working	You are not working	You aren't working	Are you working?
He is working	He's working	He is not working	He isn't working	Is he working?
She is working	She's working	She is not working	She isn't working	Is she working?
It is working	It's working	It is not working	It isn't working	Is it working?
We are working	We're working	We are not working	We aren't working	Are we working?
You are working	You're working	You are not working	You aren't working	Are you working?
They are working	They're working	They are not working	They aren't working	Are they working?

Spelling Rules

put - putting		think - thinking
run - running	**BUT**	work - working

We use Present Continuous for actions happening now.

64 **Add -ing to the verbs.**

1. read   *reading*
2. swim
3. jump
4. sit
5. walk
6. stop

> write - writing
> dance - dancing **BUT** see - seeing

65 **Add -ing to the verbs.**

1. come .*coming*...	3. take	5. have ....
2. make	4. close	6. agree ....

> play - playing   fly - flying

66 **Add -ing to the verbs.**

1. study .*studying*...	3. dry	5. say ....
2. pay	4. cry	6. try ....

67 **Add -ing to the verbs as in the example:**

1. cut .*cutting*.	6. sing	11. fight	16. watch ....
2. sit	7. make	12. clean	17. cook ....
3. read	8. kick	13. run	18. eat ....
4. drink	9. play	14. jump	19. swim ....
5. do	10. sleep	15. talk	20. dance ....

Short answers

Are you eating?	Yes, I am.
	No, I'm not.

Is | he | she | it | eating?	Yes, | he | she | it | is.
	No, | he | she | it | isn't.

Are they eating?	Yes, they are.
	No, they aren't.

68 **Write short answers.**

1. Is she sleeping? Yes, ..*she is.* ....
2. Is he reading? Yes, ...
3. Is it flying? No, ...
4. Are the boys playing football? Yes, ...
5. Is she swimming? No, ...
6. Is he driving a car? No, ...
7. Are the birds singing? Yes, ...
8. Are the monkeys eating? No, ...
9. Is the man sitting? Yes, ...
10. Are they dancing? Yes, ...
11. Is she watching T.V.? No, ...
12. Is he riding a bicycle? No, ...
13. Is he running? Yes, ...
14. Is she talking on the telephone? No, ...
15. Is the baby smiling? No, ...

69 **Look at the pictures and write as in the example:**

1. play

Long form: *..The girl is playing tennis.....*

Short form: *..She's playing tennis. ....*

2. kick the ball

....

....

3. dance

....

....

4. talk on the phone

....

....

5. jump over the fence

....

....

6. work in the garden

....

....

7. run

....

....

11. Present Continuous

70 **Write questions as in the example:**

Am	the boy	riding bicycles
Is	the women	watching T.V.
Are	Jane	cooking in the kitchen
	I	sleeping
	Jeff	eating an orange
	the girls	doing my homework

1. ..Is the boy watching T.V.? ....

2. ....

3. ....

4. ....

5. ....

6. ....

71 **Ask questions as in the**

example:

...Is Tom cleaning his room?........
Yes, Tom is cleaning his room.

1 ....
Yes, I am washing the dishes.

2. ....
Yes, they are sleeping.

3. ....
Yes, Mother is drinking coffee.

4. ....
Yes, they are doing their homework.

5. ....
Yes, Father is reading a newspaper.

6. ....
Yes, he is watching T.V.

72 **Write negative sentences as in the example:**

Bob is reading a newspaper. (book)   ..He isn't reading a book. ....

1. The boys are playing with the dog.(cat)   ....

2. Jim is going to school. (cinema)   ....

3. The teacher is talking to Mrs Huston. (Mrs Morton) ....

4. The men are riding horses. (bicycles)   ....

5. The girl is eating an apple. (banana)   ....

73 **Look at the pictures and put the verbs into the Present Continuous.**

It's 7 o'clock on Monday morning. The family is in the kitchen.

1. Mr and Mrs West ..*are drinking*.. (drink) coffee.
2. Grandfather .... (read) a newspaper.
3. Joe .... (go) to school.
4. The cat and the dog .... (eat).

It's 5 o'clock on Monday afternoon and the family is in the living room.

5. Mr West .... (watch) T.V.
6. Mrs West .... (talk) on the phone.
7. Joe .... (do) his homework.

It's 10 o'clock on Sunday morning. The family is in the garden.

9. Mr and Mrs West .... (sit) in the sun.
10. Joe and David .... (play) football.

74 **Look at the above pictures, cover the text and say what the family is doing.**

75 **Now look at the pictures again. Ask and answer each other questions then write 4 sentences as in the example:**

1. *What are Mr and Mrs Green doing in the 1st picture? They are drinking coffee.*
2. ....
3. ....
4. ....
5. ....

(76) **Look at the picture and write sentences as in the example:**

Mr Green is sleeping. *..Wrong! Mr Green isn't sleeping. He is reading a newspaper.*
The girls are playing with their dolls. *..Right! They are playing with their dolls........*

1. Mrs Green is swimming. ....

2. Grandmother is singing. ....

3. Grandfather is sleeping. ....

4. Simon is looking at the birds. ....

5. Mike is cleaning the windows. ....

6. The ducks are running. ....

7. The birds are singing. ....

8. The cat is drinking milk. ....

9. James is watering the flowers. ....

(77) **Ask and answer as in the examples:**

1. play tennis?

John: *Are they playing tennis?* ....
Greg: *No, they aren't. They're playing football.*

2. swim?

Kate: *Is she swimming?* ....
Alison: *Yes, she is. She's swimming.*.............

3. sing?

Debbie: ....
John: ....

4. write?

Judith: ....
Jenny: ....

5. sleep?

Bill: ....
Tony: ....

6. dance?

Anna: ....
Chris: ....

(78) Write negative sentences as in the example:

They / not / play / in the garden now.   *.They aren't playing in the garden now..*

1. The cat / not / drink milk.   ....
2. The children / not / do / their homework.   ....
3. I / not / listen / to the radio now.   ....
4. You / not / watch / T.V. now.   ....
5. She / not / work / in the garden now.   ....

(79) Write sentences as in the example:

The children / have / breakfast.   *.The children are having breakfast.....*

1. She / watch T.V.   ....
2. They / come / out of the house.   ....
3. Mary / write / a letter?   ....
4. The boys / run / to school.   ....
5. Mother / make / a cake.   ....
6. The girls / sit / in the living room?   ....
7. We / not / go / to the cinema.   ....
8. Tom and Jane / sing / a song?   ....
9. My brother / not / listen / to the radio.   ....
10. They / clean / the house?   ....
11. Jim / ride / a bicycle.   ....

Game 4

Your teacher divides the class into two groups. He then asks a student (the leader) to come to the front of the class. The leader writes on a piece of paper what he / she is doing (e.g. I am swimming). The students, by asking questions, try to guess. The group which finds out what is written on the paper wins 1 point.

Group A S1:   Are you cooking?
Leader: No, I'm not.
Group B S1:   Are you drinking water?
Leader: No, I'm not.
Group A S2:   Are you swimming?
Leader: Yes, I am.

Group A wins one point. Your teacher may choose another leader and you can play the game again.

12. Simple Present

Every day

Robert usually **walks** to school in the morning.

Today

But today Robert is late. He **is running** to school.

Affirmative	Negative		Interrogative
	Long form	**Short form**	
I like	I do not like	I don't like	Do I like?
You like	You do not like	You don't like	Do you like?
He likes	He does not like	He doesn't like	Does he like?
She likes	She does not like	She doesn't like	Does she like?
It likes	It does not like	It doesn't like	Does it like?
We like	We do not like	We don't like	Do we like?
You like	You do not like	You don't like	Do you like?
They like	They do not like	They don't like	Do they like?

We use Simple Present for permanent or habitual actions. happening now.

Short answers

Do you like apples?	Yes, I do.
	No, I don't.
Does he she it like apples?	Yes, he she it does.
	No, he she it doesn't.
Do they sleep?	Yes, they do.
	No, they don't.

Spelling: 3rd person singular

verbs ending in:

ss, sh, ch, x, o ➡ + es

I dre**ss** - he dre**sses**
I g**o** - he g**oes**

consonant + y ➡ ies

I tr**y** - he tr**ies**

BUT

I pla**y** - he pla**ys**

12. Simple Present

(80) **Complete the sentences as in the example:**

Simon's routine day

1. 2. 3. 4.

5. 6. 7.

1. Simon .. *lives* ... (live) in London.
2. He .... (work) in a school.
3. He .... (start) work at 8.30.
7. He .... (go) to bed at 10 o'clock in the evening.

4. He .... (stop) work at 2 pm.
5. He .... (have) lunch at 2.30.
6. He .... (read) books in the afternoon.

(81) **Look at the pictures and answer the questions.**

1. 2. 3. 4.

1. What does Alison do in the morning? ....
2. What does she do at noon? ....
3. What does she do in the afternoon? ....
4. What does she do in the evening? ....

(82) **What do you do every day? Write four sentences:**

1. ....

2. ....

3. ....

4. ....

(83) **Ask and answer questions as in the examples :**

	go to school	play the piano	like fish
Mary	✔		
Andy		✔	✔
Sally + Ben	✔		✔
You			

..*Does Mary go to school?*.. *Yes, she does.*.............................
..*Does Mary play the piano?*.... *No, she doesn't.*........................
..*Does Mary like fish?*.......... *No, she doesn't.*.......................

1. ....

....

....

2. ....

....

....

Write about you:

3. ..*Do you go to school?*... .

....

....

12. Simple Present

84 Complete the sentences as in the example:

Long form

Short form

We ..*do not* ..... like fish.   We ..*don't* ...... like fish.

1. She .... eat chicken.   She .... eat chicken.
2. I .... drive a car.   I .... drive a car.
3. They .... do their homework. They .... do their homework.
4. You .... live in Italy.   You .... live in Italy.
5. He .... play tennis.   He .... play tennis.

85 Look at the table and write what they like and what they don't like.

	chicken	fish	burgers	eggs	pizza
Caroline	✔	✔			✔
Ted		✔		✔	
Tom + Jack	✔		✔		✔
Mother	✔		✔		✔
Father	✔	✔		✔	
You					

1. ..*Caroline likes chicken, fish and pizza.* ....
   ..*She doesn't like burgers or eggs.* ....
2. ....
   ....
3. ....
   ....
4. ....
   ....
5. ....
   ....

Write about you:

6. I ....

....

86 **Look again at exercise 85. Ask and answer questions as in the example:**

..Does Caroline like eggs?....... No, she doesn't. ....
..Does Caroline like chicken? .... Yes, she does. ....

1. ....
2. ....
3. ....
4. ....
5. ....
6. ....
7. ....
8. ....
9. ....
10. ....

87 **Write one sentence for each person as in the example:**

I	do	English
Ian	like	football on Sunday
You	swim	very well
Mother	play	their homework every day
They	speaks	burgers
Mary and Tony	listens	to the radio in the morning

1. *..I play football on Sunday. ....*
2. ....
3. ....
4. ....
5. ....
6. ....
7. ....

88 **Match the pictures with the sentences.**

1. Father usually cleans the car.
2. Bob usually feeds the dog.
3. Mother usually goes shopping.

4. Sue usually takes the dog for a walk.
5. Grandfather usually works in the garden.
6. Grandmother usually cooks our dinner.

USUALLY

1. . . . . 2. . . . . 3. . . . .

. . . .

4. . . . . 5. . . . . 6. . . . .

. . . .

89 **Now look at the pictures and write what each person is doing today.**

TODAY

1. Bob *..is cleaning....* 2. Sue . . . . 3. Grandfather . . . .
   ..the car today..... . . . .

4. Mother . . . . 5. Father . . . . 6. Grandmother . . . .

. . . .

90 **Write what they usually do and what they are doing today.**

USUALLY	TODAY

1. ... *He usually drives a car.* ....   2. ... *He is riding a bicycle today.* ....

3. ....   4. ....

5. ....   6. ....

7. ....   8. ....

9. ....   10. ....

11. .... 12. ....

13. .... 14. ....

15. .... 16. ....

Game 5

Your teacher will divide the class into two groups. Group A asks misleading questions about Simon (look at exercise 80). Group B answers the questions. When mistakes are made, groups lose points.

Group A S1:	Does Simon watch TV at 5 o'clock?
Group B S1:	No, he doesn't. He reads a book.
Group A S2:	Does Simon stop work at 12 o'clock?
Group B S2:	No, he doesn't. He stops work at 2 o'clock.
Group A S3:	Does Simon goes to bed at 10 o'clock?
Teacher:	Wrong! Not goes. Does Simon go ....

Group A loses 1 point. Group B is the winner. Play the game again but this time Group B asks questions and Group A answers them.

Revision III

91 **Look at the picture and write sentences as in the example:**

1. Father *is watching T.V.*   2. Mother . . . .   3. The girls . . . .
. . . .   4. The dog . . . .   5. Jim . . . .

92 **Write negative sentences as in the example:**

Jenny / write / a letter.　　*Jenny isn't writing a letter.* . . . .

1. Jim / play / football.　　. . . . .

2. Father / drive / a car.　　. . . . .

3. Rick and I / watch / television.　. . . . .

4. I / listen / to records.　　. . . . .

5. The monkeys / climb / the trees.　. . . . .

93 **Ask and answer as in the example:**

Pam / pen.　　*Has Pam got a pen? Yes, that's her pen. It's hers.* . . . .

1. He / camera.　　. . . . .

2. You / badge.　　. . . . .

3. We / car.　　. . . . .

94) Ask questions as in the example:

Mr Smith / eat / apples.   *Does Mr Smith eat apples?* ....

1. you / go / school.   ....
2. Mary / like / pizza.   ....
3. Jim / have / bicycle.   ....
4. Jim and Mary / read / books.   ....
5. Tom / ride / horse.   ....

95) Put the verbs into the "Present Continuous" or "Simple Present".

1. Tom usually *drinks* (drink) coffee, but today he *is drinking* (drink) tea.
2. She .... (not / like) beer.
3. Look! He .... (drive) very fast.
4. The baby .... (sleep) now.
5. .... (you / want) a pizza?
6. She .... (be) a dancer.
7. They .... (watch) T.V. now.
8. My father .... (sing) well.
9. Mary .... (listen) to music now.
10. Look! Peter .... (swim).

96) Write the plural of the following words.

1. tomato .. *tomatoes* ..   4. woman ....   7. goose ....
2. baby ....   5. mouse ....   8. fish ....
3. tooth ....   6. child ....   9. foot ....

97) Underline the correct word as in the example:

He is (my, mine) father.

1. This house is (their, theirs).
2. This is (our, ours) dog. The dog is (our, ours).
3. This is Jane's coat. It's (her, hers) coat.
4. Tina is (your, yours) friend.
5. These are (my, mine) books. They are (mine, my).
6. This is (him, his) radio.
7. These are (her, hers) shoes.
8. These are (my, mine) pens. They are (my, mine).

98 **Change into the plural as in the example:**

He is a man.
...They are men...

1. This is a balloon.

....

2. It is a baby.

....

3. She is a woman.

....

4. This is a mouse.

....

5. The child is playing.

....

6. That is a wolf.

....

7. He is a policeman.

....

8. That is a goose.

....

9. This is a foot.

....

10. There is a sheep.

....

11. This is a tooth.

....

12. It is a deer.

....

99 **Fill in "I", "you", "he", "she", "it", "we" or "they".**

1. Lydia   *she* ....
2. Father and Mother ....
3. George   ....

4. you and Sue ....
5. the book ....
6. you and I ....

7. radio ....
8. the cups ....
9. Ann ....

100 **Fill in "am", "is" or "are".**

1. She .. *is* .... my sister.
2. They .... my friends.
3. I .... a good boy.
4. Ben .... my brother.

5. How .... you?
6. I .... in the garden.
7. Sally and I .... friends.
8. It .... a dog.

101 **Look at the pictures and write sentences as in the example:**

1. Mary   bag

This is Mary's bag.....
It's her bag..........
This bag is hers. ......

2. Sam   car   ....
                                                    ....
                                                    ....

3. Grandpa   house   ....
                                                    ....
                                                    ....

4. the girls   ball   ....
                                                    ....
                                                    ....

5. the policeman   dog   ....
                                                    ....
                                                    ....

6. Mother   radio   ....
                                                    ....
                                                    ....

102 **Choose the correct item.**

1. ... *This is* ..... my pencil.
   A) These are B) They are C) This is

2. Mr Smith .... to work.
   A) is walking B) walk C) are walking

3. Look! John .... his bicycle.
   A) is riding B) riding C) rides

4. .... you a dancer?
   A) Is B) Are C) Am

5. This isn't your book. It's ....
   A) mine B) my C) him

6. .... mother is a teacher.
   A) We B) Our C) She

7. They .... in a big house.
   A) is living B) lives C) live

8. He .... his breakfast now.
   A) eat B) is eating C) eats

9. Sam .... drive a car.
   A) can't B) isn't C) hasn't got

10. Be quiet! Father ....
    A) sleep B) sleeps C) is sleeping

11. She .... as a singer.
    A) works   B) work   C) is working

12. They .... lunch now.
    A) is having   B) are having   C) have

13. Look at them! They .... football.
    A) play   B) plays   C) are playing

14. He .... work in a bank.
    A) doesn't   B) hasn't   C) don't

(103) What does Carol do every day? Ask and answer as in the example:

Monday

Tuesday

Wednesday

Thursday

Friday

Saturday

1. *What does Carol do on Monday?*   *She works in the garden.*
2. ....
3. ....
4. ....
5. ....
6. ....

(104) Put the verbs in brackets into the Simple Present or Present Cont.

Saturday at Tina's House

TOM : What .... you .... (do) Tina?

TINA : I .... (write) a letter to my friend. I usually .... (do) this every Saturday.

TOM : Where .... (be) your mother?

TINA : She .... (work) in the garden.
       She always .... (cut) the grass on Saturday.

TOM : I .... (look) out of the window, now. I .... (watch)
       your father. He .... (clean) his car.

TINA : I know, he always .... (clean) his car on Saturday
       and .... (help) my mother in the garden, too.

TOM : Your family .... (work) very hard every Saturday!

13. Question Words
Who - Whose - What - When - Where

105 Fill in "who", "whose", "what", "when" or "where".

1. ...*Where* ...? in the park
2. ....?Jane's
3. ....? a table
4. ....? at 6 o'clock
5. ....? at school
6. ....? the doctor
7. ....? on Sunday

8. ....? Peter
9. ....? a horse
10. ....? at night
11. ....? today
12. ....? Julie
13. ....? a snake
14. ....? John's

15. ....? at noon
16. ....? Mother
17. ....? Father's
18. ....? at Christmas
19. ....? on Tuesday
20. ....? in the room
21. ....? in May

106 Fill in "who", "whose", "what", "when" or "where".

1. .. *What* .. is it? It's a monkey.
2. .... are you going? To the park.
3. .... is your birthday? May the 1st.
4. .... is your pen? Here it is.
5. .... are they? They're Jane and Pam.
6. .... is your school? It's near here.
7. .... are those shoes? They're mine.

8. .... time is it? It's four o'clock.
9. .... is Father? He's in the garden.
10. .... do you get up? At 7 o'clock.
11. .... are they? They're teachers.
12. .... are they? They're my parents.
13. .... do you have lunch? At noon.
14. .... are you? I'm George.

15. .... is this man? He's Mr Jones.
16. .... is your name? Jennifer.
17. .... are the zebras? At the zoo.

18. .... is this book? It's Ann's.
19. .... are they? They're lions.
20. .... is it? It's mine.

107 **Choose the correct item.**

1. .. *Who* . is this woman? Mrs Newton.
   A) Who   B) Whose   C) What

2. .... hat is it? It's Mary's.
   A) Where   B) Whose   C) What

3. .... do they like? They like chocolate.
   A) Who   B) Where   C) What

4. .... is she going? To the shops.
   A) Who   B) When   C) Where

5. .... do you play football? On Sunday.
   A) Who   B) When   C) What

6. .... are my glasses? In your bedroom.
   A) Where   B) What   C) Who

7. .... is your mother's name? Liz.
   A) Who   B) Whose   C) What

8. .... is on the telephone? Mrs Sheldon.
   A) Whose   B) Who   C) What

9. .... are the children? At the zoo.
   A) Who   B) Where   C) Whose

10. .... are they? They're snakes.
   A) Who   B) Where   C) What

11. .... do you go swimming? In summer.
   A) What   B) When   C) Where

12. .... is this ball? It's Tom's.
   A) Whose   B) What   C) Who

13. .... is the baby? In the bedroom.
   A) Whose   B) Who   C) Where

14. .... are those animals? They're cows.
   A) Who   B) What   C) Whose

15. .... is this car? It's my father's.
   A) Who   B) What   C) Whose

16. .... is your birthday? In April.
   A) When   B) Where   C) Whose

108 **Fill in "who", "whose", "what", "when" or "where".**

1. ... *Whose* .. is this car? It's my father's.
2. .... do you live? In Madrid.
3. .... is your name? Chris.
4. .... do you leave work? At 2.00.
5. .... is he? Our new teacher.
6. .... is it? It's a hen.
7. .... car is it? It's Ted's.
8. .... is your brother? At school.
9. .... is his name? Stephen.
10. .... does he go to school? At 8.30.

14. Prepositions of Place
At, Into, In, Behind, Under, On, Near, In Front of, Over

At

Into

In

Behind

Under

On

Near

In Front of

Over

At home

At school

At work

At the theatre

At the cinema

At the zoo

109 **Look at the picture and fill in the blanks.**

1. There is a sofa, two armchairs and three chairs .. *in* ... the living room.

2. There is a table and there is a vase .... the table.

3. There is a T.V. set .... a small table.

4. There is a window .... the door.

5. There is a picture .... the wall.

6. There is a table .... the picture and a telephone .... the table.

7. There is a man .... the window.

8. There is a cat .... the sofa.

9. An old woman is coming .... the living room.

110 **Now write about the living room in your house.**

111 **Look at the picture and fill in the blanks.**

There is a bed 1) .. *in* .. the bedroo
There is a table 2) ...... the bedroom
There are some books 3) .... th
table and there is a bag 4) ...... th
table. There is a chair 5) .... the
bedroom. The chair is 6) .... th
bed and there is a picture 7) ......
the wall. There is a cat 8) .... th
bed. There are two shoes
9) .... the bed 10) .... the
floor. There is a small table 11)
.... the bed. A dog is coming 12) .... the room.

112 **Look at the picture and fill in the blanks.**

There is a woman 1) ...... the house. There is a man standing 2) ...... the door. He has got
bottle 3) .... his hands. A boy is sitting 4) .... a tree. There is a boy 5) .... a
horse. There are some ducks 6) .... the horse. There is a dog 7) .... the
girl. There is a bird flying 8) .... the girl's head. There is a cat 9) .... the woman.

Game 6 In the Kitchen

Your teacher will ask a student to come to the front of the class. He will be the leader of the game. The leader must write in his / her book where the mouse is. (e.g. The mouse is near the cheese.) Then the teacher divides the class into two groups. The groups ask the leader questions in turn until they find the mouse. The winning group is the one which finds the mouse.

example: Group A S1: Is the mouse under the table?
Leader: No, it isn't.
Group B S1: Is the mouse behind the radio?
Leader: No, it isn't.
Group A S2: Is the mouse near the cheese?
Leader: Yes, it is.

Group A wins 1 point. Now the teacher can choose another leader and you can play the game again.

15. Prepositions of Time

In the morning	**At noon**	**On Sunday**

Jane goes to school in the morning.	She has lunch at noon.	She goes to the park on Sunday.

IN	AT	ON
in the morning	at 8 o'clock	on Sunday (days)
in the afternoon	at noon	on Monday
in the evening	at night	on Tuesday
in November (months)	at midnight	on Wednesday etc.
in summer (seasons)	at Eid	on October 4th (dates)
in 1992 (years)	at Christmas	on Sunday afternoon

(113) Fill in "in", "at" or "on".

1. .. *at* .. 6 o'clock
2. ...... night
3. ...... Wednesday
4. 1987
5. ...... November 20th
6. ...... winter
7. ...... Monday

8. ...... the afternoon
9. ...... Friday afternoon
10. ...... midnight
11. ...... Eid
12. ...... spring
13. ...... Christmas
14. ...... Friday

15. 1990
16. ...... December
17. ...... autumn
18. ...... the evening
19. ...... Monday evening
20. ...... 3 o'clock
21. ...... noon

(114) Fill in "in", "at" or "on".

1. .. *On* .. Monday morning
2. ...... the morning
3. ...... night
4. ...... Wednesday night
5. ...... the afternoon
6. ...... Tuesday afternoon
7. 1821

8. ...... 12 o'clock
9. ...... spring
10. ...... December 25th
11. ...... Friday
12. ...... May 1st
13. ...... the evening
14. ...... Tuesday evening

15. 1912
16. ...... January
17. ...... midnight
18. ...... summer
19. ...... February 2nd
20. ...... 7 o'clock
21. ...... May

(115) Fill in "in", "at" or "on".

1. Ann's birthday is ...*on*...... May 5th.
2. We have breakfast .... the morning.
3. We have lunch .... noon.
4. We have dinner .... the evening.
5. He usually goes to the park .... Sunday afternoon.
6. They usually play tennis .... Saturday.
7. We usually go swimming .... summer.
8. We usually have breakfast .... 8 o'clock .... the morning.
9. It is cold .... winter.
10. It is rainy .... autumn.

(116) Fill in "in", "at" or "on".

1. She goes shopping ...*on*..... Saturday morning.
2. They start work .... 8.30 .... the morning.
3. Her birthday is .... July 19th.
4. Children usually get presents .... Christmas.
5. It's hot .... summer.
6. He usually stays at home .... the evening.
7. John usually does his homework .... the afternoon.
8. Mother and Father go to church .... Sunday.
9. Father usually works in the garden .... Saturday afternoon.
10. Mother's birthday is .... March 10th.

(117) Choose the correct item.

1. We go to bed ..*at*.. midnight.
   A) on   B) in   C) at

2. Mother usually works ...... the morning.
   A) on   B) in   C) at

3. School starts ...... September.
   A) on   B) in   C) at

4. They usually go to work ...... 8 o'clock.
   A) on   B) in   C) at

5. Children don't go to school ...... Sunday.
   A) on   B) in   C) at

6. We send cards ...... Christmas.
   A) on   B) in   C) at

7. We usually watch T.V. ...... the evening.
   A) on   B) in   C) at

8. My birthday is ...... April 15th.
   A) on   B) in   C) at

9. We go skiing ...... Easter.
   A) on   B) in   C) at

10. Al goes to the pub ...... Tuesday evening.
    A) on   B) in   C) at

16. How many - How much

How **much** cheese is there on the table? Not **much**.
How **many** apples are there? Not **many**.
How **much** bread is there? Not **much**.

Countable plural nouns		Uncountable singular nouns	
eggs	bags	sugar	money
apples	girls	coffee	lemonade
chairs	boys	cheese	bread
pens	glasses	butter	milk
books	radios etc.	water	meat etc.

How many + countable nouns		How much + uncountable nouns	
How many	girls glasses ? boys	How much	money bread ? sugar

118 **Write "C" for countable nouns and "U" for uncountable nouns.**

1. .. *C* ... elephants
2. .... milk
3. .... helicopters
4. .... snakes
5. .... coffee
6. .... sugar
7. .... lions
8. .... hats

9. .... monkeys
10. .... children
11. .... bread
12. .... dresses
13. .... shoes
14. .... money
15. .... doctors
16. .... meat

17. .... trains
18. .... boxes
19. .... water
20. .... beds
21. .... cheese
22. .... doors
23. .... teeth
24. .... butter

119 Fill in "How many" or "How much" as in the example:

1. . How many ... books are there on the table?
2. .... money have you got?
3. .... sugar is there on the table?
4. .... oranges are there on the table?
5. .... shoes are there on the floor?
6. .... windows are there in the room?
7. .... milk is there in the bottle?
8. .... men are there in the room?
9. .... butter is there in the fridge?
10. .... bread is there on the table?
11. .... orange juice is in the bottle?
12. .... flowers are there in the vase?
13. .... pencils have you got?
14. .... coke is there in the bottle?

120 Fill in "How many" or "How much" as in the example:

1. . How many ... ears have you got?
2. .... toys have you got?
3. .... coffee is there on the table?
4. .... bananas are there on the table?
5. .... money is it?
6. .... water is there on the table?
7. .... rooms are there in the house?
8. .... butter is there on the table?
9. .... biscuits have you got?
10. .... policemen can you see?
11. .... glasses are there on the table?
12. .... cheese have you got?
13. .... pictures are there on the wall?
14. .... cars can you see?
15. .... lemonade is there in the bottle?

16. How many – How much

(121) **Ask and answer questions as in the example:**

1. .. How many radios can you see? I can see three radios. . . . .
   .. How much are they? They are £15 each. . . . .

2. . . . .
   . . . .

3. . . . .
   . . . .

4. . . . .
   . . . .

5. . . . .
   . . . .

6. . . . .
   . . . .

7. . . . .
   . . . .

17. Some - Any

some + countable or uncountable noun (in affirmative sentences)	any + countable or uncountable noun
There are **some tomatoes**. There is **some bread**.	Are there **any oranges**? Is there **any milk**? No, there isn't **any milk**.

(122) Fill in "some" or "any" as in the example:

1. Are there ... *any* .... rabbits in the garden?

2. Are there . . . . children in the class?

3. There aren't . . . . chairs in the room.

4. Are there . . . . birds in the tree?

5. There isn't . . . . money in the bag.

6. There is . . . . coffee in the cup.

7. There are . . . . policemen in the police station.

8. There are . . . . fish in the water.

9. Are there . . . . oranges in the basket?

10. There isn't . . . . milk in the fridge.

17. Some – Any

 Look and write.

1. men
2. boys
3. flowers
4. desks
5. oranges
6. books
7. girls
8. monkeys
9. pictures
10. schoolbags
11. mice

1. .....Are there any men in the classroom? ....
   ....No, there aren't any men in the classroom. ....
2. ....Are there any boys in the classroom? ....
   ....Yes, there are some boys in the classroom. ....
3. ....
   ....
4. ....
   ....
5. ....
   ....
6. ....
   ....
7. ....
   ....
8. ....
   ....
9. ....
   ....
10. ....
    ....
11. ....
    ....

124 **Write what they have got and what they haven't got.**

	tomatoes	potatoes	meat	bread
Teresa	✔		✔	✔
Richard + Jenny	✔	✔	✔	
Mark		✔	✔	✔
Sally	✔		✔	✔

1. ...*Teresa has got some tomatoes, some meat and some bread*......... ...*but she hasn't got any potatoes.*..........................

2. Richard and Jenny ....
....

3. Mark ....
....

4. Sally ....
....

↻ Revision IV

125 **Change to the plural.**

1. box   .. *boxes* ....
2. man   ....
3. orange   ....
4. duck   ....
5. church   ....
6. balloon   ....
7. star   ....

8. knife   ....
9. baby   ....
10. bus   ....
11. child   ....
12. fish   ....
13. foot   ....
14. brush   ....

15. lady   ....
16. sheep   ....
17. watch   ....
18. radio   ....
19. mouse   ....
20. shoe   ....
21. ox   ....

126 **Fill in "am", "is" or "are".**

1. You ... *are* ... a teacher.
2. Michael .... eleven years old.
3. It .... an elephant.
4. They .... cows.
5. I .... a girl.

6. Jill .... my sister.
7. They .... mice.
8. It .... a box.
9. We .... friends.
10. They .... doctors.

127 Fill in "a", "an" or "---".

1. *an* aeroplane	9. ...... men	17. ...... flower	25. ...... eye
2. ...... car	10. ...... elephant	18. ...... umbrella	26. ...... books
3. ...... chairs	11. ...... baby	19. ...... shoes	27. ...... bottle
4. ...... glass	12. ...... iron	20. ...... hand	28. ...... star
5. ...... frog	13. ...... armchair	21. ...... mice	29. ...... lady
6. ...... bus	14. ...... birds	22. ...... foot	30. ...... knife
7. ...... onion	15. ...... tree	23. ...... apple	31. ...... girls
8. ...... animal	16. ...... octopus	24. ...... tomato	32. ...... eagle

128 Put the verbs into the "Simple Present" or "Present Continuous".

1. Look at the boys! They ... *are playing* ..... (play) football.

2. This .... (be) a photograph of my friend.

3. John .... (have) a wonderful camera.

4. Mother .... (water) the plants every day.

5. She always .... (dance) at the disco.

6. Look! The monkey .... (climb) the tree.

7. Quiet! I .... (listen) to the radio now.

8. Look! He .... (smile) at me.

9. Jane .... (get up) at 8 o'clock every morning.

10. Stop! A car .... (come).

11. She .... (take) the bus to school every day.

12. Where .... (be) Father? He .... (sit) in the kitchen.

13. Listen! Tina .... (sing) in the bathroom.

14. I .... (watch) television now.

15. Peter .... (go) to the cinema every weekend.

129 Fill in "in", "on", "at" or "into".

1. She works. *in* .. an office.

2. ...... Sunday she goes to church.

3. ...... the evening she goes swimming.

4. He stays ...... home ...... the afternoon.

5. He goes to bed ...... midnight.

6. I do my homework ...... the afternoon.

7. He is ...... work now.

8. The picture is ...... the wall.

9. The cat is coming ...... the kitchen.

10. There is some cheese ...... the fridge.

(130) Change to the plural as in the example:

She is a nurse. *They are nurses.*

1. He is a man. .... 6. He is a boy. ....
2. He is a teacher. .... 7. She is a girl. ....
3. This is a mouse. .... 8. It is an elephant. ....
4. That is an apple. .... 9. This is a lion. ....
5. It is a table. .... 10. That is a bottle. ....

(131) Fill in "some" or "any".

1. There isn't .. *any* .. bread on the table. 6. There are .... fish in the lake.
2. I want .... flowers. 7. Is there .... milk?
3. He hasn't got .... money. 8. Are there .... birds in the tree?
4. Is there .... bread in the fridge? 9. There are .... apples on the table.
5. There are .... men in the garden. 10. There aren't .... mice in the house.

(132) Fill in "How many" or "How much".

1. .. *How many* .... eggs are there on the table?
2. .... money have you got?
3. .... girls are there in the class?
4. .... sugar have you got?
5. .... boxes are there on the table?
6. .... meat do you want?
7. .... cheese is there in the fridge?
8. .... shirts has he got?
9. .... bread is there on the table?
10. .... flowers are there in the garden?
11. .... brothers have you got?
12. .... lemonade do you want?
13. .... cats have you got?
14. .... pens are there on the desk?
15. .... coffee is there on the table?
16. .... cars are there in the street?

(133) **Put the verbs into the "Present Continuous" or "Simple Present".**

1. The boy ... *is drinking* ..... (drink) coffee now.

2. She .... (sit) on the sofa.

3. Mother .... (read) the newspaper.

4. I .... (sleep) at night.

5. He .... (go) to school at 9.00 am.

6. I .... (watch) television every day.

7. I .... (write) a letter now.

8. He usually .... (walk) to school.

9. Sue .... (make) a cake. She can't talk to you now.

10. Jane .... (come) home now.

(134) **Choose the correct item.**

1. Where is the cat? It is .. *on* .... the sofa.
   A) on   B) in   C) at

2. He usually .... football on Sunday.
   A) plays   B) play   C) is playing

3. The .... are playing in their room now.
   A) tables   B) chairs   C) children

4. The vase is .... the table.
   A) at   B) in   C) on

5. I get presents .... Christmas.
   A) under   B) on   C) at

6. This hat is ....
   A) she   B) her   C) hers

7. The flowers are .... the vase.
   A) behind   B) in   C) at

8. This is John. .... is my brother.
   A) I   B) He   C) She

9. Ben .... now. He is tired.
   A) sleep   B) sleeps   C) is sleeping

10. My parents .... shopping on Saturday morning.
    A) go   B) goes   C) is going

11. He is going .... the bedroom.
  A) into B) on C) at

12. Jane .... a book now.
  A) reads B) read C) is reading

13. .... books are there in the box?
  A) How much B) Many C) How many

14. Are there .... bottles of coca-cola in the fridge?
  A) any B) some C) a

15. Where is Mother? She .... a shower.
  A) has B) are having C) is having

16. Mike always .... in the sea in the summer.
  A) swims B) is swimming C) swim

17. Father usually .... to the radio.
  A) is listening B) listen C) listens

18. I can't see .... flowers in the picture.
  A) any B) a C) some

19. Hurry up! The bus ....
  A) is coming B) comes C) coming

20. Listen! Who .... in the garden?
  A) sings B) sing C) is singing

21. They .... to church every Sunday.
  A) go B) goes C) are going

22. Where are Chris and Sally? They .... in the park.
  A) walks B) walk C) are walking

23. I .... comics in bed every night.
  A) am reading B) is reading C) read

24. Smile! Father .... our photograph.
  A) is taking B) takes C) take

25. Have you got .... biscuits?
  A) a B) any C) some

26. .... is he? Mr Jones.
  A) Who B) Where C) Whose

27. He .... his homework now.
  A) do B) does C) is doing

135 **Look at the picture, then ask and answer as in the examples:**

(boys) .. *Are there any boys in the park?* ....
.. *Yes, there are some boys. How many boys can you see? I can see three.*

(horses) .. *Are there any horses in the park?* ....
.. *No, there aren't any horses.* ....

1. (women) ....

....

2. (ducks) ....

....

3. (penguins) ....

....

4. (girls) ....

....

5. (monkeys) ....

....

6. (men) ....

....

7. (cars) ....

....

8. (dogs) ....

....

(136) Fill in "some" or "any".

1. Are there .. *any* ... bottles in the fridge?

2. There is .... butter in the fridge.

3. Are there .... chocolates in the box?

4. There is .... salad on the table.

5. There are .... biscuits in the kitchen.

6. There isn't .... tea on the table.

7. Are there .... buses in the bus station?

8. There aren't .... bicycles in the park.

9. There are .... zebras in the zoo.

10. There isn't .... water in the bottle.

(137) Fill in "who", "what", "when", "whose" or "where".

1. .. *Where* .... is the milk? It's on the table.

2. .... is he? He's my father.

3. .... colour are your eyes? They're blue.

4. .... do you live? I live in Paris.

5. .... is your birthday? May 2nd.

6. .... is that in the tree? It's a cat.

7. .... is Roy? He's in the garden.

8. .... is your friend's name? Cathy.

9. .... are you? I'm Ben's friend.

10. .... is the cheese? It's on the table.

11. .... is this dress? It's mum's.

12. .... does school start? In September.

138 **Put the verbs into the "Simple Present" or "Present Continuous".**

It (1) .... (be) 10 o'clock. The baby (2) .... (sleep).Mother (3) .... (visit) friends now and Father (4) .... (paint) the fence. John (5) .... (play) football with his friends. I (6) .... (do) my homework. I (7) .... (be) a student and I (8) .... (go) to school every day. I (9) .... (want) to be a doctor.

139 **Put the verbs into the "Simple Present" or "Present Continuous".**

Every day my father (1) .... (get) up at 7:30. He (2) .... (have) breakfast at 8:00 and then he (3) .... (go) to work. He (4) .... (be) a teacher. He (5) .... (come) back at 2:00 and we (6) .... (have) lunch. Then he (7) .... (sleep) for an hour. In the afternoon he (8) .... (watch) TV. But today he (9) .... (not/watch) TV. He (10) .... (help) my mother in the kitchen. We (11) .... (have) a party. It (12) .... (be) my birthday. I (13) .... (be) ten years old.

140 **Antonio goes to his new school. His teacher asks him some questions. Write what questions he asks him.**

Teacher: Hi! I'm your new teacher. (1) ... *Who are you?* ....

Antonio: I'm Antonio.

Teacher: (2) ....

Antonio: I come from Italy.

Teacher: (3) ....

Antonio: I'm ten years old.

Teacher: (4) ....

Antonio: No, I haven't got any brothers but I've got a sister.

Teacher: (5) ....

Antonio: Her name is Maria.

141 **To revise Prepositions of Place play game 6 p.69.**

Pre-Test 1 (Units 1 - 4)

A Fill in **a** or **an**.

1 .... book 2 .... onion 3 .... armchair 4 .... dog

5 .... fish 6 .... eye 7 .... car 8 .... lemon

9 .... octopus 10 .... eagle 11 .... man 12 .... horse

13 .... banana 14 .... aeroplane 15 .... owl 16 .... bird

B Change to the plural.

17 one cow - two .... 18 one baby - two .... 19 one leaf - two ....

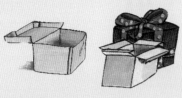  

20 one box - two .... **21** one knife - four .... **22** one rabbit - four ....

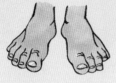 

23 one foot - two .... **24** one fish - two .... **25** one sheep - two ....

26 one child - two .... **27** one brush - two .... **28** one man - two ....

 Fill in he, she, it, we or they.

29 Sally	....	**35** Sally and I	....	**41** book	....
30 girls	....	**36** women	....	**42** girl	....
31 houses	....	**37** Tom and Sally	....	**43** flowers	....
32 Ben	....	**38** elephant	....	**44** helicopter	....
33 snake	....	**39** men	....	**45** policemen	....
34 woman	....	**40** Tom and I	....	**46** boy	....

 Fill in am, is or are.

47 It .... a bus.

48 He .... a teacher.

49 I .... a student.

50 They .... doctors.

51 It .... a book.

52 He .... a policeman.

53 Tom .... a doctor.

54 She .... English.

55 It .... a bicycle.

56 They .... sharks.

57 He .... a doctor.

58 We .... friends.

59 I .... a policeman.

60 She .... a dancer.

61 They .... books.

62 It .... an orange.

E Change to the plural.

63 It is a mouse. ....

64 She is a woman. ....

65 It is a dolphin. ....

66 He is a doctor. ....

67 I am a dancer. ....

68 You are a teacher. ....

69 She is a student. ....

70 It is a fox. ....

71 You are a policeman. ....

72 It is a house. ....

F Answer the questions with short answers.

73 Is it a radio?

74 Are they torches?

75 Are they fish?

76 Is it a dolphin?

77 Is she a girl?

78 Is it a book?

79 Is it a house?

80 Are they men?

Pre-Test 2 (Units 1 - 8)

A Fill in This, These, That or Those.

1 .... are books. 👉

2 .... is a house. 👉

3 .... is a cat. 👉

4 .... is a chair. 👉

5 .... are men. 👉

6 .... are fish. 👉

B Ask and answer as in the example:

e.g. (Ann/pencil)
Has Ann got a pencil?
Yes, she has.
It's her pencil.
It's hers.

7 (she/cat)
....
....
....
....

8 (they/hats)
....
....
....
....

9 (he/car)
....
....
....
....

10 (you/dog)

....
....
....
....

12 (she/balloon)

....
....
....
....

11 (he/umbrella)

....
....
....
....

C Underline the correct item.

13 This is Tom's car. It's **hers**/**his**.

14 These are **their**/**theirs** books.

15 This hat is **her**/**hers**.

16 They are **our**/**ours** dogs.

17 She is **my**/**mine** friend.

18 This is **their**/**theirs** school.

19 Those flowers are **her**/**hers**.

20 This is Father's piano. It's **his**/**hers**.

D Choose the correct item.

21 .... father is a teacher.

   A Sally's   **B** Sally   **C** Sallys'

22 That is .... egg.

   A a   **B** this   **C** an

23 This is .... dog.

   A I   **B** my   **C** mine

24 This car is ....

   A mine   **B** my   **C** I

25 She .... a television.

   A have got **B** has got **C** is

26 They .... dolphins.

   A is   **B** are   **C** am

27 .... a cat on the wall.

   A There is   **B** They are **C** There are

28 There are four .... in the kitchen.

   A women's **B** woman's **C** women

29 This is Mary's radio. It's ....

   A she   **B** her   **C** hers

30 Is .... a teacher?

   A it   **B** him   **C** he

31 This is .... ball.

   A John   **B** John's   **C** Johns'

32 I .... seven years old.

   A are   **B** is   **C** am

33 This is .... snake.

   A a   **B** an   **C** that

34 That is Ben's hat. It's ....

   A his   **B** hers   **C** ours

35 There are two .... in the garden.

   A cat   **B** cats   **C** cat's

36 .... four cakes on the table.

   A There are **B** They are **C** There is

37 Mark .... a new car.

   A is   **B** has got **C** have got

38 He .... a policeman.

   A am   **B** is   **C** are

39 Susan is .... sister.
    A ours   **B** mine   **C** my

40 Are .... children?
    A she   **B** he   **C** they

E Fill in **There is** or **There are**.

41 .... two children in the park.
42 .... a man in the room.
43 .... two cats under the tree.
44 .... a dog under the table.
45 .... two books on the table.
46 .... a picture on the wall.
47 .... four cars in the street.
48 .... a lion at the zoo.

F Fill in **a** or **an**.

49 .... pencil
50 .... apple
51 .... lion
52 .... iron

53 .... radio
54 .... armchair
55 .... octopus
56 .... plane

57 .... eagle
58 .... owl
59 .... orange
60 .... house

G Fill in **he, she, it, we** or **they**.

61 Are these your books? Yes, ... are.
62 Where is Father? .... is at work.
63 Is this your dog? Yes, ... is.
64 Is Jane five? No, ... isn't.
65 Are you and Anne sisters? No, ... aren't.
66 Are the children here? Yes, ... are.
67 Who is Sally? .... is my friend.
68 Are these your records? No, ... are his.
69 Is this a bird? No, ... isn't.
70 Are you and Tom friends? Yes, ... are.
71 Is Mother here? Yes, ... is.
72 Are they teachers? Yes, ... are.

H Fill in **am, is** or **are**.

73 John and Sally .... students.
74 They .... children.
75 Mary .... a teacher.
76 I .... a girl.

77 He .... a policeman.
78 They .... at school.
79 I .... a good boy.
80 Mother .... in the sitting room.

Pre-Test 3 (Units 1 - 12)

(A) Ask and answer with can.

1 (they/sing)

....

....

2 (he/jump)

....

....

3 (he/play football)

....

....

4 (he/walk)

....

....

5 (he/ride a horse)

....

....

6 (he/climb)

....

....

7 (they/swim)

....

....

8 (it/run)

....

....

(B) Write the plural of the following words:

9 lady .... **11** knife .... **13** man ....

10 church .... **12** mouse .... **14** tomato ....

(C) Ask and answer as in the example:

e.g.: **Tony/book** *Has Tony got a book? Yes, that's his book. It's his.*

15 Helen/radio ....

16 You/umbrella ....

17 They/box ....

18 He/ball ....

19 Mary/balloon ....

20 You/watch ....

21 Mark/plane ....

22 They/horse ....

D **Match the following to the pictures.**

A Please don't talk!
B Let's paint the room.
C Let's wash the car.
D Clean your room, please!

E Let's watch TV.
F Take an umbrella, please!
G Wash your hands, please!
H Drink your milk, please!

23 ....

24 ....

25 ....

26 ....

27 ....

28 ....

29 ....

30 ....

E **Put the verbs in brackets into the present continuous or the present simple.**

31 Mother usually .... **(drink)** coffee in the afternoon.
32 Look! He .... **(climb)** the tree.
33 He .... **(do)** his homework now.
34 Listen! Father .... **(sing)** in the garden.
35 Pierre .... **(come)** from France. He is French.

36 The dolphins .... (**play**) with a ball now.
37 Peter .... (**go**) to the supermarket on Fridays.
38 Mother .... (**read**) the newspaper now.
39 He often .... (**drive**) to work.
40 She usually .... (**go**) to the zoo on Sundays.
41 Father .... (**write**) a letter now.
42 She .... (**cut**) in the grass now.
43 Look! It .... (**snow**).
44 She .... (**tidy**) her room now.
45 The children .... (**play**) tennis now.
46 Listen! Mother .... (**play**) the piano.
47 The girls .... (**swim**) in the sea now.
48 He usually .... (**start**) work at 9:30.
49 Ann .... (**visit**) her grandmother every week.
50 He usually .... (**go**) to church on Sundays.

(F) Underline the correct item.

51 **That/Those** is Eva's car.
52 Mother **sleep/is sleeping** now.
53 **Does/Can** they drive?
54 Is it an egg? Yes, it **is/are**.
55 Father **isn't/hasn't** at home.
56 Lions **can/can't** fly.
57 These are **child/children**.
58 She **doesn't/don't** work in a school.
59 He **haven't got/hasn't got** a book.
60 This bike is **his/her**.

61 This is **my/mine** ball.
62 **These/This** are radios.
63 That is **Sally/Sally's** doll.
64 Father **is painting/paints** the bathroom.
65 These are **tooth/teeth**.
66 This balloon is **his/her**.
67 **Can/Does** you swim?
68 Is she a doctor? Yes, she **is/am**.
69 Do you play football? Yes, I **do/don't**.
70 He **have got/has got** two cats.

(G) Choose the correct answer.

71 That is .... car.
   A Marks'   B Mark's   C Mark
72 .... my friends.
   A These are B It is   C We are
73 She .... to the park every Sunday.
   A go   B is going   C goes
74 We .... our homework now.
   A do   B are doing C is doing
75 Alice .... drive a car.
   A can't   B hasn't got C isn't

76 Tom .... black hair.
   A can't   B isn't   C hasn't got
77 The children .... to school now.
   A are walking B walk   C walks
78 Sarah .... riding every day.
   A go   B goes   C is going
79 That is the .... ball.
   A dog   B dogs'   C dog's
80 .... four boys in the room.
   A There are   B There is   C They are

Pre-Test 4 (Units 1 - 17)

A Fill in Who, Whose, What, When or Where.

1 .... is that man? He is my father.
2 .... is it? It's a book.
3 .... is Christmas Day? December 25th.
4 .... is Mother? She is in the garden.
5 .... is that car? It's John's.
6 .... do you go to the cinema? On Sundays.
7 .... is he? He is my friend.
8 .... is this? It's a kite.
9 .... is the bag? It's Jane's.
10 .... are the girls? They are at school.

B Fill in in, at or on.

11 It is hot .... the summer.
12 My birthday is .... October 25th.
13 We go to school .... 8:30 am.
14 We go to the park .... Saturdays.
15 I leave work .... 3:00 pm.
16 They sleep .... the afternoon.
17 He eats lunch .... noon.
18 He goes to the zoo .... Sundays.
19 We go on holiday .... August.

20 My mother's birthday is .... June.
21 We don't go to school .... the summer.
22 She visits her grandmother .... Fridays.
23 It is cold .... the winter.
24 They go to the cinema ....
   Sunday afternoon.
25 My sister's birthday is .... July.
26 They give presents .... Christmas.

C Fill in How much or How many.

27 .... milk is there in the glass?
28 .... money has she got?
29 .... butter is there in the fridge?
30 .... books are there on the table?

31 .... cars can you see?
32 .... coffee is there in the jar?
33 .... boys are there in the room?
34 .... trains are there in the picture?

D Fill in some or any.

35 Is there .... jam in the jar?
36 There aren't .... biscuits on the table.
37 There are .... pens on the table.
38 Are there .... birds in the garden?
39 She has got .... books.

40 Are there .... pictures in the book?
41 There aren't ...... elephants in the circus.
42 Is there .... tea in the cup?
43 There isn't .... bread on the table.
44 She has got .... sugar.

(E) **Put the verbs in brackets into the present simple or the present continuous.**

45 Be quiet! I .... **(read)** the newspaper.
46 Mother .... **(help)** us now.
47 The students .... **(go)** to school every day.
48 Mother usually .... **(visit)** grandfather on Fridays.
49 We .... **(do)** our homework now.
50 Jane .... **(come)** from England. She is English.
51 She .... **(like)** ice cream.
52 Look! The cat .... **(climb)** up the tree!
53 He .... **(play)** football every day.
54 The baby .... **(sleep)** now.
55 I .... **(want)** to be a teacher.
56 Look! The dog .... **(run)** after Tom.
57 Mother .... **(go)** to the gym every Thursday.
58 He .... **(listen)** to music now.
59 Father .... **(come)** home at 6:00 pm every day.
60 Listen! He .... **(play)** the piano.
61 She .... **(live)** in Spain.
62 They usually .... **(go)** on holiday to France.
63 They .... **(eat)** their dinner now.
64 Listen! They .... **(sing)** now.

(F) **Choose the correct item.**

65 The man .... now.
   A sing   **B** is singing **C** sings
66 .... are dolphins.
   A That   **B** This   **C** Those
67 This is Sam's ball. It's .... ball.
   A their   **B** her   **C** his
68 A policeman is coming .... the room.
   A in   **B** into   **C** at
69 Tom has got .... aeroplane.
   A an   **B** a   **C** some
70 .... milk is there in the bottle?
   A Are there   **B** How many
   C How much
71 There is a book .... the table.
   A in   **B** at   **C** on
72 .... is this black car? It's Ben's.
   A When   **B** Whose   **C** Who

73 A man is coming .... the classroom.
   A into   **B** in   **C** at
74 This book is ....
   A his   **B** he   **C** her
75 Fish .... fly.
   A can   **B** can't   **C** have got
76 There isn't .... sugar in the bowl.
   A some   **B** a   **C** any
77 Mother is .... work.
   A at   **B** in   **C** on
78 He .... now.
   A sleeps   **B** is sleeping
   C are sleeping
79 There is a telephone .... the desk.
   A into   **B** over   **C** on
80 There's a cat .... the table.
   A into   **B** in   **C** under

Progress Test 1 (Units 1 - 2)

NAME: .... CLASS: ....

DATE: .... MARK: ....

(Time: 30 minutes)

A Fill in **a** or **an**.

1 .... egg   2 .... orange   3 .... cat   4 .... lion

5 .... horse   6 .... onion   7 .... iron   8 .... armchair

9 .... doll   10 .... eye   11 .... book   12 .... ball

B Change to the plural.

e.g. one dog - *two dogs*

13	one book	-	two	....	17 one piano	-	five	....
14	one leaf	-	four	....	18 one box	-	three	....
15	one torch	-	six	....	19 one watch	-	two	....
16	one baby	-	three	....	20 one dress	-	five	....

96

C **Fill in the plurals.**

21 one goose - two ....

22 one child - two ....

23 one man - two ....

24 one sheep - two ....

 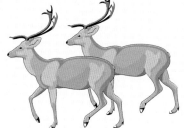

25 one deer - two ....

 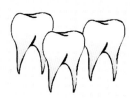

26 one tooth - three ....

27 one mouse - two ....

28 one woman - two ....

29 one fish - three ....

30 one foot - two ....

Progress Test 2 (Units 3 - 4)

NAME: .... CLASS: ....

DATE: .... MARK: ....

(Time: 30 minutes)

A Fill in **he**, **she**, **it** or **they** as in the example:

e.g. *it*

1 ....

2 ....

3 ....

4 ....

5 ....

6 ....

7 ....

B Choose the correct pronoun.

8 .... am a teacher.

   A He   **B** I   **C** They

9 .... is a clever boy.

   A She   **B** It   **C** He

10 .... is a radio.

   A He   **B** She   **C** It

11 .... are friends.

   A I   **B** We   **C** He

12 .... are flowers.

   A They   **B** You   **C** It

98

C Fill in: am, is or are.

13 They .... apples.
14 It .... a book.
15 They .... bicycles.
16 I .... a student.

17 He .... a teacher.
18 You .... my friend.
19 It .... an octopus.
20 We .... brothers.

D Answer the questions as in the examples:

e.g.  Is he a doctor?
No, he isn't.

e.g.  Is it a horse?
Yes, it is.

21  Are they dolls?
....

22  Are they oxen?
....

23  Are you a student?
....

24  Is it a dog?
....

25  Is she a nurse?
....

26 Is he a teacher?
....

E Change to the plural as in the example:

e.g. It is an umbrella. *They are umbrellas.*

27 I am a doctor. ....
28 He is a man. ....

29 It is a mouse. ....
30 You are a nurse. ....

Progress Test 3 (Units 5 - 6)

NAME: ....   CLASS: ....

DATE: ....   MARK: ....

(Time: 30 minutes)

A Fill in this, these, that or those.

1 .... is a fish

2 .... is an elephant.

3 .... are books.

4 .... is an orange.

5 .... are flowers.

6 .... are monkeys.

7 .... is a bus.

8 .... is a glass.

B Fill in There is or There are.

9 .... a bed.

10 .... six pencils.

11 .... three books.

12 .... a chair.

13 .... a dog.

14 .... a cat.

15 .... two tables.

100

C **Look at the pictures and answer as in the example:**

e.g. Are there two birds?
Yes, there are.

16 Is there one watch?
....

17 Are there three chairs?
....

18 Is there one rabbit?
....

19 Are there five balls?
....

20 Is there one glass?
....

D **Choose the correct item.**

21 There .... a man in the garden.
   A are   **B** isn't   **C** aren't

22 .... are my shoes.
   A These   **B** This   **C** That

23 There .... a book on the desk.
   A are   **B** is   **C** aren't

24 .... there two girls in the room?
   A Isn't   **B** Is   **C** Are

25 .... is an aeroplane.
   A That   **B** Those **C** These

26 There .... a dog in the garden.
   A aren't   **B** are   **C** isn't

27 .... is a chair.
   A Those   **B** This   **C** These

28 There .... two birds in the cage.
   A are   **B** is   **C** isn't

29 .... are bicycles.
   A This   **B** That   **C** Those

30 .... there a teacher in the classroom?
   A Aren't   **B** Is   **C** Are

Progress Test 4 (Units 7 - 8)

NAME: .... CLASS: ....

DATE: .... MARK: ....

(Time: 30 minutes)

 A Look at the pictures and answer as in the example:

e.g. Has she got a cat?
Yes, she has.

Have they got a car?
1 ....

Has she got a ball?
2 ....

Has he got an umbrella?
3 ....

Has he got a bicycle?
4 ....

Have they got a cat?
5 ....

Has he got a hat?
6 ....

Have they got a ball?
7 ....

B **Fill in the blanks with** have got **or** has got.

8 Paul .... a car.
9 You .... a dog.
10 We .... a house.

11 She .... an umbrella.
12 Mr Smith .... a computer.

C **Underline the correct word.**

13 This is **my/mine** house.
14 Stanley is **hers/her** father.
15 The blue dress is **your/yours**.
16 **His/He** cat is black.

17 That car is **their/theirs**.
18 This book is **our/ours**.
19 Jessica is **my/mine** sister.
20 This is **her/hers** coat.

D **Choose the correct answer.**

21 Has she got a cat? No, she ....
   A has   **B** haven't   **C** hasn't
22 That dress is ....
   A hers   **B** she   **C** her
23 Mr Smith .... got a radio.
   A haven't   **B** have   **C** hasn't
24 She .... a cat.
   A have got   **B** has got   **C** got
25 These are the .... books.
   A boys   **B** boy   **C** boys'

26 That is .... car.
   A Jenny   **B** Jenny's   **C** Jennys
27 Has he got a bicycle? Yes, he ....
   A hasn't   **B** have   **C** has
28 These shoes are ....
   A mine   **B** me   **C** I
29 These are the .... hats.
   A men's   **B** men   **C** man
30 Those shoes are ....
   A him   **B** he   **C** his

Progress Test 5 (Units 9 - 10)

NAME: .... CLASS: ....

DATE: .... MARK: ....

(Time: 30 minutes)

A Answer the questions as in the example:

e.g. Can it swim?
Yes, it can.

Can they jump?
1 ....

Can he dance?
2 ....

Can they play tennis?
3 ....

Can he drive a bus?
4 ....

Can she write?
5 ....

Can he see?
6 ....

Can he read?
7 ....

B Write sentences as in the example:

Cats can fly. *Wrong! Cats can't fly.*   Birds can fly. *Right! Birds can fly.*

8 Horses can sing.

....

9 Fish can ride bicycles.

....

10 Mice can play the piano.

....

11 Dogs can run.

....

12 Cats can jump.

....

13 Birds can write.

....

14 Sheep can drive cars.

....

15 Monkeys can climb.

....

C **Answer the questions about yourself.**

16 Can you ride a bicycle?....................... 19 Can you climb a tree? ....
17 Can you swim? .... 20 Can you play basketball? ....
18 Can you dance? ....

D **Match the following to the pictures.**

Please look at the board!   Don't run!
Please help me!   Let's watch TV.
Be careful!   Let's listen to music.
Eat your food!   Don't cry, please!
Please don't sing!   Let's go to the park.

21 .... 22 .... 23 .... 24 ....
....

25 .... 26 .... 27 .... 28 ....
....

29 .... 30 ....
....

Progress Test 6 (Units 11 - 12)

NAME: .... CLASS: ....

DATE: .... MARK: ....

(Time: 30 minutes)

A Look at the pictures and complete the sentences as in the example:

e.g. She *is playing* .... (play) tennis.

1 They .... (ride) horses.

2 She .... (watch) TV.

3 They .... (have) lunch.

4 He .... (drive) a bus.

5 They .... (run).

6 He .... (clean) the car.

7 He .... (cook).

B Complete the sentences.

David **8)** .... (live) in York. He is a doctor.

He **9)** .... (work) in a hospital. He

10) .... (start) work at 7 am.

He **11)** .... (stop) work at 5 pm.

He **12)** .... (have) dinner at

6 pm. He **13)** .... (watch) TV in the evening.

106

C **Answer the questions.**

14 Is he riding a bicycle?

Yes, ...

15 Does he live in Paris?

No, ...

16 Are they watching TV?

No, ...

17 Do they like football?

Yes, ...

18 Is she writing a letter?

No, ...

19 Does Tom work at a school?

Yes, ...

20 Are they listening to music?

Yes, ...

D **Choose the correct item.**

21 Sue .... TV every morning.

A watch   B watches   C is watching

22 My mother .... now.

A sleep   B sleeps   C is sleeping

23 Jane and Claire .... in a shop.

A work   B is working   C works

24 Paul .... breakfast every day.

A eat   B is eating   C eats

25 The boys .... football in the park now.

A play   B plays   C are playing

26 Look! The dog .... in the river.

A swims   B is swimming

C swim

27 I .... my room once a week.

A clean   B cleans

C am cleaning

28 Listen! She .... now.

A sings   B singing   C is singing

29 They .... like burgers.

A don't   B aren't   C doesn't

30 .... he washing the dishes?

A Are   B Is   C Does

Progress Test 7 (Units 13 - 14)

NAME: .... CLASS: ....

DATE: .... MARK: ....

(Time: 30 minutes)

(A) Fill in who, whose, what, when or where.

1 .... time is it? It's six o'clock.

2 .... is that man? My uncle.

3 .... book is this? It's Peter's.

4 .... is your birthday?
On May 1st.

5 .... do you live? In London.

6 .... do you go to bed?
At 10:00.

7 .... is the dog? In the garden.

8 .... is her name? Laura.

9 .... coat is this? It's Mark's.

10 .... are they? They're lions.

(B) Choose the correct item.

11 .... is that dog? Simon's.
A Who   B Whose C What

12 .... is your brother's name? Mike.
A When   B Where C What

13 .... do you go skiing? In the winter.
A When   B What   C Whose

14 .... is your school? In Smith Street.
A What   B When   C Where

15 .... is that boy? Paul.
A Who   B Where C When

16 .... pens are these? Janet's.
A Who   B Whose C What

17 .... do you eat breakfast? In the morning.
A Who   B Whose C When

18 .... is your bag? On the table.
A Where   B What   C Who

19 .... are those animals? They're horses.
A Where   B Whose C What

20 .... is John? He's in the park.
A Who   B Where C Whose

C **Look at the picture and fill in** in, on, under **or** near.

There is a sofa **21)** .... the living room. There is a table **22)** .... the sofa. There are some flowers **23)** .... the table and there is a ball **24)** .... the table. There is a chair **25)** .... the table. There is a carpet **26)** .... the floor.

D **Look at the picture and fill in** on, near, in **or** under.

There is a table **27)** .... the kitchen. There is a basket **28)** .... the table and a cat **29)** .... the table. There is a glass **30)** .... the basket.

Progress Test 8 (Units 15 - 17)

NAME: ....   CLASS: ....

DATE: ....   MARK: ....

(Time: 30 minutes)

Ⓐ Choose the correct item.

1 He goes to bed .... midnight.
    A on   **B** in   **C** at

2 I usually read a book .... the evening.
    A on   **B** in   **C** at

3 We go to school .... Mondays.
    A on   **B** in   **C** at

4 She comes home .... six o'clock.
    A on   **B** in   **C** at

5 My birthday is .... June 25th.
    A on   **B** in   **C** at

6 It's cold .... the winter.
    A on   **B** in   **C** at

7 They go to the cinema .... Saturdays.
    A on   **B** in   **C** at

8 He gets up .... seven o'clock.
    A on   **B** in   **C** at

9 We eat our dinner .... the evening.
    A on   **B** in   **C** at

10 We go to the beach .... the summer.
    A on   **B** in   **C** at

Ⓑ Fill in How many or How much.

11 .... children are there in the classroom?

12 .... apples are there on the table?

13 .... cheese is there in the fridge?

14 .... lemonade is in the bottle?

15 .... chairs are there in the room?

16 .... books have you got?

17 .... bread is there on the table?

18 .... sugar do you want?

19 .... coffee is there in the jar?

20 .... cats has she got?

Fill in **some** or *any*.

21 There aren't .... apples in the fridge.

22 There is .... cheese in the fridge.

23 Is there .... meat in the fridge?

24 There isn't .... bread in the fridge.

25 There aren't .... oranges in the fridge.

26 There are .... bananas in the fridge.

27 Are there .... eggs in the fridge?

28 There are .... tomatoes in the fridge.

29 There isn't .... lemonade in the fridge.

30 Are there .... lemons in the fridge?

Word List

A

add
adjective
affirmative
afternoon
again
age
agree
always
American
animal
answer
any
April
armchair
at
August
autumn

B

badge
bar
basket
bathroom
be quiet
bedroom
behind
below
besides
bicycle
bird
birthday
birthday cake
black
blank
blue
bottle
box
bracket
bread
breakfast
brother
brush
burger
bus
but

C

cage
camel
camera
can
chair
change
cheese
chicken
choose
Christmas
classroom
clean
climb
close
clown
cold
come back
come from
come out of
comics
command
consonant
cook
correct
countable
cow
cry
cup
cut

D

dancer
date
day
December
dig
dinner
disco
dish
divide
doctor
dolphin
donkey
dress
drive

dry
duck

E

eagle
Easter
eleven
end
English
evening
every
example

F

family
far
farm
February
feed
fence
fight
find
floor
flower
fly
following
football
form
Friday
friend
frog

G

game
girl
glasses
go shopping
go to bed
good
grandfather
grandmother
Greek

group
guess

H

hand
hard
hen
her
hers
his
home
how many
how much
hungry

I

imperative
in
in front of
in order to
in turn
interrogative
into
invite
iron
irregular
Italian
item
its

J

January
Japanese
July
jump
June

K

kick
kitchen
knife